PRAISE FOR

LEGO NINJAGO

GARMADON

"Garmadon... is an exciting new foray into the expansive world of LEGO® NINJAGO®, exploring new facets of the world, and its rich tapestry of characters."

-JAY'S BRICK BLOG

"Tri Vuong's writing and art make this new addition to the Ninjago universe fun and compelling. Longtime LEGO fans and new readers will both get a kick out of this exciting adventure."

-CBR

"Vuong uses everything that has come before effectively and in a way that's not overwhelming for new readers. It's very new reader friendly in fact... The comic feels visually perfect for its audience no matter their age."

-GRAPHIC POLICY

"The highlight of Vuong's work on this comic is easily the art. It's reminiscent of Stan Sakai with patient storytelling, and it also features multiple references to Kurosawa. Simply put, this is a story that plays well visually."

-COMICS BOOKCASE

"For NINJAGO fans it really is an essential read, adding to the already rich history of the much loved LEGO theme."

-BRICKS FANZ

PRAISE FOR

LEGO NINJAGO

SHATTERSPIN

"LEGO NINJAGO: SHATTERSPIN #1 is another solid start for those who are Ninjago fans, enjoy action, or martial arts excitement."

-GRAPHIC POLICY

"Tri Vuong is an excellent story teller whether it be with words or with pictures."

-NERD INITIATIVE

For my brothers.

CAMERON CHITTOCK

For Henry, George, Reuben, Sammy,
Ada, Mabel, Monty and Roland.

WILL MORRIS

LEGO NINJAGO

STRIKE OF THE SERPENTINE

CAMERON CHITTOCK
WRITER

WILL MORRIS
ARTIST

SARA ANTONELLINI
COLORIST

PAT BROSSEAU
LETTERER

SKYBOUND COMET

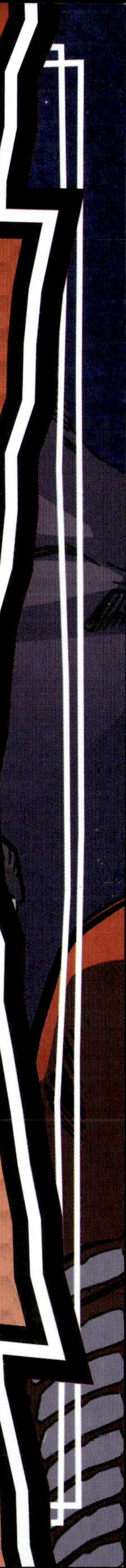

CHAPTER 1
ALLIANCES

NINJAGO.
NOW.
IT IS LATE IN THE SEASON TO SEE SUCH A FLOWER IN BLOOM. ALL THE MORE REASON TO APPRECIATE ITS SIGHT.
IT'S GOOD TO SEE YOU, OLD FRIEND.
I ADMIT, I WAS SURPRISED TO HEAR FROM YOU, WU. AFTER EVERYTHING THAT HAPPENED.
THE WORLD HAS CHANGED QUITE A BIT SINCE WE LAST CROSSED PATHS.
MUCH OF IT FOR THE BETTER, I HOPE.
BUT I FEAR THE PROGRESS WE'VE MADE MIGHT NOT LAST MUCH LONGER.

I HAVE FACED SO MANY TRIALS IN MY YEARS, I'M NOT SURE WHAT SCARES ME MOST. THAT OUR GREATEST CHALLENGES MIGHT STILL BE AHEAD...
...OR THAT I NO LONGER HAVE WHAT IT TAKES TO MEET THEM.
IT DOESN'T MATTER HOW MANY VICTORIES YOU ACHIEVE, **DOUBT** WILL ALWAYS LINGER.
THAT IS WHY I SEEK YOUR COUNSEL. YOU HAD A GIFT FOR SEEING UPCOMING DANGERS WITH A CLARITY OF PURPOSE.
DID I? EVEN **NOW** I HAVE DOUBTS ABOUT WHAT HAPPENED ALL THOSE YEARS AGO.
I LOSE SLEEP, QUESTIONING WHAT WE COULD HAVE DONE DIFFERENTLY, OR IF IT WAS ALL WORTH IT. I THINK THAT'S TRUE OF ANY GREAT CONFLICT...
...BUT ESPECIALLY **THE SERPENTINE WAR.**

THEN.
THANK YOU FOR JOINING ME, MYSTAKE. I WAS WORRIED I MIGHT HAVE TO MAKE THIS JOURNEY ALONE.
RUMORS OF TURMOIL, WHISPERS OF UNREST, SHADOWY FIGURES UP TO NO GOOD. IT SHOULD BE FUN, WU!
THOUGH, I KNOW THERE ARE OTHER COMPANIONS YOU MIGHT HAVE PREFERRED.
GARMADON IS ON HIS OWN PATH NOW, WHEREVER THAT MIGHT TAKE HIM. BUT I'M NOT SURE HE SHARED MY CONCERN IN THIS MATTER.
IT'S ONLY YOUR BROTHER THAT YOU MISS?
MISAKO IS ANOTHER STORY. ONE FOR ANOTHER DAY, PERHAPS.
OUR INVESTIGATION SHOULD KEEP US BUSY IN THE MEANTIME.

HELLOOO? ANYONE HOOOME?
LOCKED DOORS AND BARRED WINDOWS. MAYBE THIS VILLAGE **HAS** SEEN DARK DAYS. AND IF THE RUMORS **ARE** TRUE...
...WE MIGHT NOT FIND A **WARM WELCOME.**
YOU'RE NOT THE FIRST TRESPASSERS TO COME INTO OUR VILLAGE UNINVITED. WE WEREN'T READY THEN...
...BUT THIS TIME, **NO ONE** IS WALKING AWAY.

PLEASE--
WE DO NOT WISH
TO HURT YOU!
OR
TAKE FROM
YOU!
WE'RE HERE
TO HELP! BUT
WE WILL NOT BE
DEFENSELESS,
EITHER.
NINJA--
--GO!
C-CAN YOU?
ACTUALLY
HELP US?
ONLY IF
YOU SHOW
US WHAT'S
WRONG.

IF THERE WAS EVER AN EMERGENCY, THIS IS WHERE THE VILLAGE KEPT EVERYTHING WE'D NEED. NOT A LOT, BUT THE NECESSITIES.
MEDICAL SUPPLIES, FOOD RATIONS--JUST IN CASE.
BUT, ALSO... ARMOR AND WEAPONS.
DOESN'T MATTER ANYMORE.
NEED A LOT OF THOSE OUT HERE?
THERE'S NOTHING LEFT.

THE ENTIRE STOCKPILE WAS STOLEN?
WE TRIED TO FEND THE THIEVES OFF..
"...BUT WE WERE OUTNUMBERED AND CAUGHT OFF GUARD."
ANY IDEAS AS TO WHO THESE PEOPLE MIGHT HAVE BEEN?
IT WAS NIGHT, AND IT ALL HAPPENED SO FAST. IT WAS HARD TO GET A GOOD LOOK.
"BUT WHOEVER ATTACKED US...THEY WEREN'T HUMAN."
UNLESS YOU KNOW FOLKS WHO HISS.
DON'T FINISH THAT ACCUSATION UNLESS YOU'RE SURE OF WHAT YOU SAW. THE RIPPLE EFFECTS COULD SPAN ALL OF NINJAGO.
I'D NEVER SEEN ONE UP CLOSE BEFORE, BUT THESE WERE SERPENTINE. AND IF THEY'RE HITTING SMALL OUTFITS LIKE OURS...

"...WHO KNOWS WHAT ELSE THEY HAVE IN MIND."
HUMANS OF NINJAGO-- BEWARE!
TERRIBLE HORRORS ARE ON THE HORIZON! THE GOLDEN MASTER IS COMING, AND IT WILL BRING DOOM TO NINJAGO!
NO ONE WILL BE SAFE UNLESS WE ACT!
WILL YOU ANSWER THE CALL?!
...
WELL DONE, STRIKE. ANOTHER ROUSING RECEPTION.

THIS WAS A MISTAKE.
SO, GO BURROW UNDERGROUND OR SOMETHING. IT'S NOT LIKE YOU'RE ANY HELP UP HERE.
YOU THINK I'M THE PROBLEM? IT'S THE VENOMARI WHO KEEP SCARING HUMANS AWAY. WASTING OPPORTUNITIES.
SPEAK TO ME LIKE THAT AGAIN, AND I'LL WASSSSTE YOU, YOU LOUSY EXCUSE FOR A SNAKE!
ENOUGH OF THIS--I'LL JUST MAKE THEM LISTEN TO US.
NO!
THAT WON'T GET US ANYWHERE. NOT IN THE LONG TERM.
WHEN WE WERE CHILDREN, THE ELDERS WOULD TELL US SCARY STORIES. WE'D HIDE UNDER THE BED OR TURN THEM INTO GAMES TO MAKE THEM SEEM LESS REAL.
BUT THEY ARE REAL NOW. AND THERE WILL BE NO HIDING FROM WHAT THE GOLDEN MASTER UNLEASHES UNLESS WE STOP IT.
THE ONLY WAY WE DO THAT, IS IF WE WORK TOGETHER.

UH HUH. OR WE CAN QUIT WHILE WE'RE AHEAD. I'M DONE.
TURNS OUT THE CONSTRICTAI AND I CAN AGREE ON SOMETHING.
WAIT-- PLEASE!
WE CAN'T GIVE UP! YOU KNOW WHAT WILL HAPPEN IF WE FAIL!
IT WAS A GOOD TRY, STRIKE. BUT THE HUMANS DON'T WANT TO LISTEN.
MAYBE IT'S FOR THE BEST THAT THEY DON'T HEED OUR WARNING. WHAT HAVE THEY EVER DONE FOR US?
MAYBE THEY'LL GET WHAT THEY DESERVE.
IT WON'T JUST BE THEM. YOU WON'T BE SPARED EITHER!
NONE OF US WILL BE.
"WE'RE HERE BECAUSE WE HAVE REASON TO BELIEVE THE SERPENTINE ARE ORGANIZING."

VILLAGES ACROSS NINJAGO HAVE FOUND THEIR DEFENSES WEAKENED AND THEIR WEAPONS STOLEN. THE EVIDENCE POINTS IN ONE DIRECTION.
AS THE SON OF THE FIRST SPINJITZU MASTER, IT'S MY RESPONSIBILITY TO DEFEND NINJAGO, AND I HOPE TO FIND OTHERS WITH ABILITIES LIKE YOURS TO HELP ME.
THE LOST MELODY MUSIC HALL.
HM. I DON'T LIKE THE SOUND OF THAT.
YOU WON'T HELP? BUT--
NO-- LISTEN. DO YOU HEAR THAT?
...
I DON'T HEAR ANYTHING, SONO.
BEING MASTER OF SOUND MEANS HARNESSING THE POWER OF THE PERFECT NOTE AND PITCH. THAT REQUIRES SHARPENED SKILLS OF LISTENING.
DO YOU KNOW WHAT I HEAR?
THE REALM OF NINJAGO GETTING READY, TUNING ITS INSTRUMENTS. WHETHER IT'S TO PLAY A MILITARY MARCH OR PEACEFUL SYMPHONY, I CANNOT SAY.
THERE'S ONLY ONE WAY TO FIND OUT. YES, I WILL JOIN YOUR BUDDING ENSEMBLE.

THE ROAD OF MANY NAMES.
AS WE SEARCH FOR THE TRUTH, I CAN THINK OF MANY USES THIS ELEMENTAL MASTER MIGHT LEND US.
THE ABILITY TO APPEAR AS SOMEONE ELSE COULD BE INVALUABLE.
FRIENDS, UP THIS WAY!
IF WE CAN FIND HIM, OF COURSE.
OH, I DON'T KNOW...
...HE MAY BE CLOSER THAN YOU THINK!
YOU ARE THE MASTER OF FORM?! BUT WHERE IS MYSTAKE?
SHE SAID SHE HAS HER OWN WAYS OF HELPING THE CAUSE. I MERELY STEPPED INTO THE ROLE IN HER STEAD.
IT SOUNDS LIKE THERE ARE MANY PARTS YOU MIGHT NEED ME TO PLAY, IF WE'RE TO FEND OFF THE SERPENTINE THREAT.
I CANNOT PROMISE IT WILL BE EASY, LEO. OR SAFE.
I HAVE NO DOUBT. SOMETHING TELLS ME IT WILL REQUIRE THE PERFORMANCE OF A LIFETIME!

THE NORTHERN MOUNTAIN PASS.
I'VE HEARD ENOUGH.
BUT I BARELY TOLD YOU ANYTHING, BENTON.
RAHHH!
I'M SICK AND TIRED OF CLEARING ROADS AND STACKING ROCKS. I HAVE ALL THESE POWERS, AND THERE'S NOTHING FOR ME TO DO!
I SHOULD BE OUT THERE, PROVING MY WORTH! FINDING DANGER AND GLORY!
TAKE ME TO THE ACTION. BECAUSE IF I HAD BEEN THERE DURING ONE OF THESE ATTACKS...

"...THE SERPENTINE WOULD BE GOING HOME EMPTY HANDED."
I DON'T THINK ANY WISH COULD SOLVE WHAT'S TO COME.
IT'S A SHAME YOUR STIRRING SPEECH FELL ON SUCH DEAF EARS!
BUT YOU HAD OUR UNDIVIDED ATTENTION.
REALLY?
OH YES, OH YES. ABSOLUTELY!
YOU CAN CALL ME MASTER CHEN. THIS IS MY ASSOCIATE CLOUSE.
WE DON'T IGNORE MATTERS OF IMPORTANCE.
AND SOMETHING TELLS ME YOU, STRIKE, ARE IMPORTANT. VERY IMPORTANT!

I DON'T FEEL IMPORTANT.
YES. **THAT** IS THE POINT! THEY WANT YOU TO THINK THEY DON'T CARE AT ALL ABOUT THE GOLDEN MASTER OR PROPHECIES OR **ANYTHING!**
BUT THEY DO. OH YES, THEY DO.
IF THEY **DIDN'T**, HOW COME THEY ARE SO FASCINATED WITH SERPENTINE HISTORY?
IF THEY ARE, THEY HAVE A FUNNY WAY OF SHOWING IT.
MAYBE YOU'RE NOT LOOKING HARD ENOUGH, HM?
IF YOU START OPENING YOUR EYES, YOU'LL SEE ARTIFACTS FROM YOUR ANCESTORS "PRESERVED" ALL AROUND.
"PRESERVED" IS SIMPLY A FANCY WORD FOR **"STOLEN"**.

WHY STEAL THEM? BECAUSE THESE ARTIFACTS AREN'T MERELY TRINKETS. NO, NO, THEY'RE SO MUCH MORE!
"THEY'RE PART OF THE SERPENTINE STORY. THE GOOD, THE BAD AND, YES...THE PROPHECIES.
"LIKE THE COMING OF THE GOLDEN MASTER!
"THE ONE WHO WILL REACH HEIGHTS OF POWER NOT SEEN SINCE THE FIRST SPINJITZU MASTER. THE ONE WHO WILL BRING UNIMAGINABLE TURMOIL TO THE WORLD...

"ALL OF NINJAGO, PAWNS IN HIS DOMINATION. PRISONERS. NO CHOICE, NO FREE WILL. ONLY SUFFERING FOR THE SERPENTINE.
"BUT IN MY STUDIES, I'VE SEEN THAT SOME OF YOUR ANCESTRAL ARTIFACTS POSSESS GREAT POWER. THEY MIGHT BE THE ONLY WAY TO AVOID THIS CALAMITY!"
MAYBE THAT'S WHY THE HUMANS KEEP THEM FROM THE SERPENTINE, HM?

AND THIS IS JUST WHAT THEY DISPLAY FOR ALL TO SEE! HUMANS TEND TO KEEP THE TRUTH UNDER VEIL. HEHEH.
WHAT ELSE DO THEY HAVE, THAT THEY'RE NOT SHOWING US?
"YOU WOULDN'T BELIEVE YOUR GLOWING RED EYES."
OH...YOU...DIDN'T KNOW THIS WAS HAPPENING?
NO. I DIDN'T.
AH, SORRY-- I CAN NEVER REMEMBER WHAT'S A BIG SECRET AND WHAT'S NEWS. SILLY MR. CHEN, SPILLING THE BEANS.
BUT WHAT CAN YOU DO, HUH?
...
WE CAN CALL THEIR BLUFF. IF THEY REALLY DON'T CARE ABOUT THE GOLDEN MASTER, THEN WHY NOT ASK FOR THE ARTIFACTS BACK?
OOOH, NOW THERE'S AN IDEA. WHAT DO YOU THINK, CLOUSE?
I WONDER IF THAT IS SOMETHING YOUR FRIENDS FROM THE OTHER TRIBES COULD ALL AGREE ON?
YES. I WONDER, I WONDER.

THE EMERALD FOREST.
I THINK WE'VE COME TO THE RIGHT PLA--
WHA--?!
KRAK!
KRKK!
UNLESS YOU'VE CHANGED YOUR TUNE SINCE RECRUITING THE OTHERS...

...I'D SAY YOU'VE VERY MUCH LOST YOUR WAY.
PLEASE, MASTER OF NATURE, IF YOU'LL LISTEN TO WHAT I HAVE TO SAY-- HNN--YOU MIGHT UNDERSTAND WHAT'S AT STAKE!
OH, I DO. PERHAPS BETTER THAN ANY OF YOU.
YOU'RE AFRAID OF SOMETHING THAT MIGHT HAPPEN. FEAR CAN SPROUT REACTIONS FAR WORSE THAN THE INITIAL SEED.
THERE'S NO NEED FOR THESE VINES--WE ARE NOT YOUR ENEMY!
WE SIMPLY HOPE THAT A SHOW OF UNITY BETWEEN THE ELEMENTAL MASTERS WILL DETER ANY CONFLICT FROM STARTING!
LET HER USE HER VINES, WU!
I CAN STILL CALL THE EARTH TO AID ME!
SNAP
IT ONLY PROVES THAT WE DON'T NEED HER ANYWAY!

AS MASTER OF EARTH, I'M JUST AS CONNECTED TO THE GRASS BENEATH OUR FEET AS YOU ARE, BROOK.
BUT **UNLIKE** YOU, I STAY GROUNDED IN **REALITY**.
IT MIGHT COME TO IT THAT THE ONLY WAY FOR US TO KEEP NINJAGO SAFE IS **ALL OUT WAR**. AND IF SO...
I SAY BRING IT ON.
IF THAT'S TO BE THE CASE, THEN YOU WILL DO SO WITHOUT ME.
YOUR GROUP IS STRONG. THE LEAVES AND ROOTS FROM ALL CORNERS OF NINJAGO TELL ME IT'S STILL GROWING.
BUT IF IT IS A **WAR** YOUR ALLIANCE SEEKS, TREAD CAREFULLY. YOU MIGHT NOT LIKE WHAT YOU FIND.
BAH, DON'T LISTEN TO HER. THE ONLY THING FOR US TO FIND IS MORE RECRUITS.

WHAT BRINGS US ALL OF US TRIBAL LEADERS HERE?
IF I HAVE TO BE STUCK WITH THE OTHERS, I SHOULD AT LEAST KNOW WHY.
TRUST ME, THERE IS NO REASON GOOD ENOUGH.
MY NAME IS STRIKE, AND I'M THE ONE WHO REQUESTED THIS AUDIENCE.
I MIGHT BE ANACONDRAI, BUT I DON'T SPEAK FOR MY TRIBE. AS YOU ALL KNOW, WE ARE...HESITANT TO MINGLE OUTSIDE OUR OWN KIND.
I HOPE MY ATTEMPT TO DO SO SHOWS THE SERIOUSNESS OF THE ISSUE AT HAND.

THE GOLDEN MASTER IS COMING, AND IT WILL MARK THE TRUE END OF THE SERPENTINE.
I FOR ONE REFUSE TO SIT BY AND DO NOTHING. THE HUMANS WON'T HELP, SO IT'S UP TO US.
YOU ALL LOOK AT EACH OTHER AND SEE DIFFERENCES. OLD RIVALRIES. POTENTIAL THREATS.
BUT WE ARE ALL SERPENTINE.
I'VE DISCOVERED THAT REMNANTS OF OUR HISTORY HAVE BEEN LOST. STOLEN. THESE ARTIFACTS MIGHT BE THE KEY TO AVOIDING THE PROPHECY.
I SUGGEST WE GET THEM BACK FROM THE HUMANS. AS A WAY TO REMEMBER WHAT BINDS US, AND WITH ANY LUCK...
...SEND A MESSAGE.
I KNOW WHAT MESSAGE I'D SEND THE HUMANS!
IF WE WERE TO GO ALONG WITH THIS, WHERE WOULD WE START?
JAMANAKAI VILLAGE. IT'S CITED IN OUR TEXTS AS THE "HOME TO STORIES". MAYBE IT CAN BE A SYMBOL FOR STARTING A NEW CHAPTER.
WE WILL MEET RESISTANCE.
DON'T YOU ALL SEE? IF WE WORK TOGETHER...

"...WHO WOULD EVEN THINK OF STANDING UP TO US?"

CHAPTER 2
FANNING THE FLAMES

ALL THESE TRIBES MAKE QUITE THE SHOW, BUT WHAT'S YOUR GAME, STRIKE?
IT MIGHT BE HARD FOR YOU TO UNDERSTAND, PYTHOR, BUT NOT EVERYTHING'S A GAME.
THAT'S MERELY A MATTER OF PERSPECTIVE.
AND DEMANDING THE RETURN OF THE SERPENTINE ARTIFACTS SCATTERED ABOUT THEIR TOWNS WILL BRING THEM TO YOUR CAUSE?
THE HUMANS IGNORED OUR WARNINGS ABOUT THE COMING OF THE GOLDEN MASTER.
IT BRINGS THEM LISTENING. WHICH WILL GET US ONE STEP CLOSER TO BEING PREPARED FOR WHAT'S COMING.
IN THE END, IT WILL TAKE ALL OF US. THE HUMANS AND SERPENTINE.
BUT YOU DON'T HAVE ALL THE SERPENTINE. NOT THE ANACONDRAI. YOU OFFER A YARD SALE WHEN WHAT THEY WANT IS A FIGHT!
THEN THEY'RE SURE TO BE DISAPPOINTED.
CARE TO PUT THAT THEORY TO THE TEST?
I'LL TALK TO THE ELDERS, SEE IF WE MIGHT FOLLOW THIS MARCH...JUST FAR ENOUGH TO WATCH.

"THEN WE CAN SEE FOR OURSELVES WHAT SORT OF RECEPTION THE HUMANS PROVIDE."
THE ELEMENTAL ALLIANCE CAMP.
THANK YOU FOR COMING, MISAKO. IT'S...WONDERFUL TO SEE YOU.
AND I SEE THAT YOU MADE FRIENDS, WU.
YES, THESE ELEMENTAL MASTERS HAVE ANSWERED MY CALL ON NINJAGO'S BEHALF.
THEY'RE QUITE THE COMPANY.
I HAVE TO BELIEVE GARMADON WILL JOIN US. I DON'T FEEL LIKE MYSELF WITHOUT HIM.
I KNOW WHAT YOU MEAN. BUT I'M HERE TO HELP IN THE MEANTIME.
I CAN TELL YOU THAT PEOPLE SENSE SOMETHING COMING. SOMETHING BIG.
I THINK THE SERPENTINE WOULD QUALIFY.
WELL, FOR MOST FOLKS, "BIG" MEANS THEY'LL BE SWEPT UP OR CAST ASIDE.

IF THE SERPENTINE REALLY ARE AT THE HEART OF THIS UNEASE, YOU SHOULD FOCUS YOUR ATTENTION HERE--JAMANAKAI VILLAGE.
MORE THAN ONE TRIBE OF SERPENTINE WAS SEEN HEADED THAT WAY...IF THE RUMORS ARE TO BE BELIEVED.
THEN WE MUST ACT QUICKLY, IF WE'RE TO KEEP THIS FROM ESCALATING ANY FURTHER.
SURELY WITH THIS ALLIANCE YOU'VE FORMED, NINJAGO WILL STAND A FIGHTING CHANCE AGAINST THE SERPENTINE.
MY HOPE IS THAT BY BEING TOGETHER, WE AVOID HAVING TO FIND OUT.
SOME OF OUR GROUP WOULD WELCOME THE CHANCE TO PROVE YOU RIGHT...
...BUT I FEAR NINJAGO WOULD NOT BE THE SAME ON THE OTHER SIDE. AND NEITHER WOULD WE.

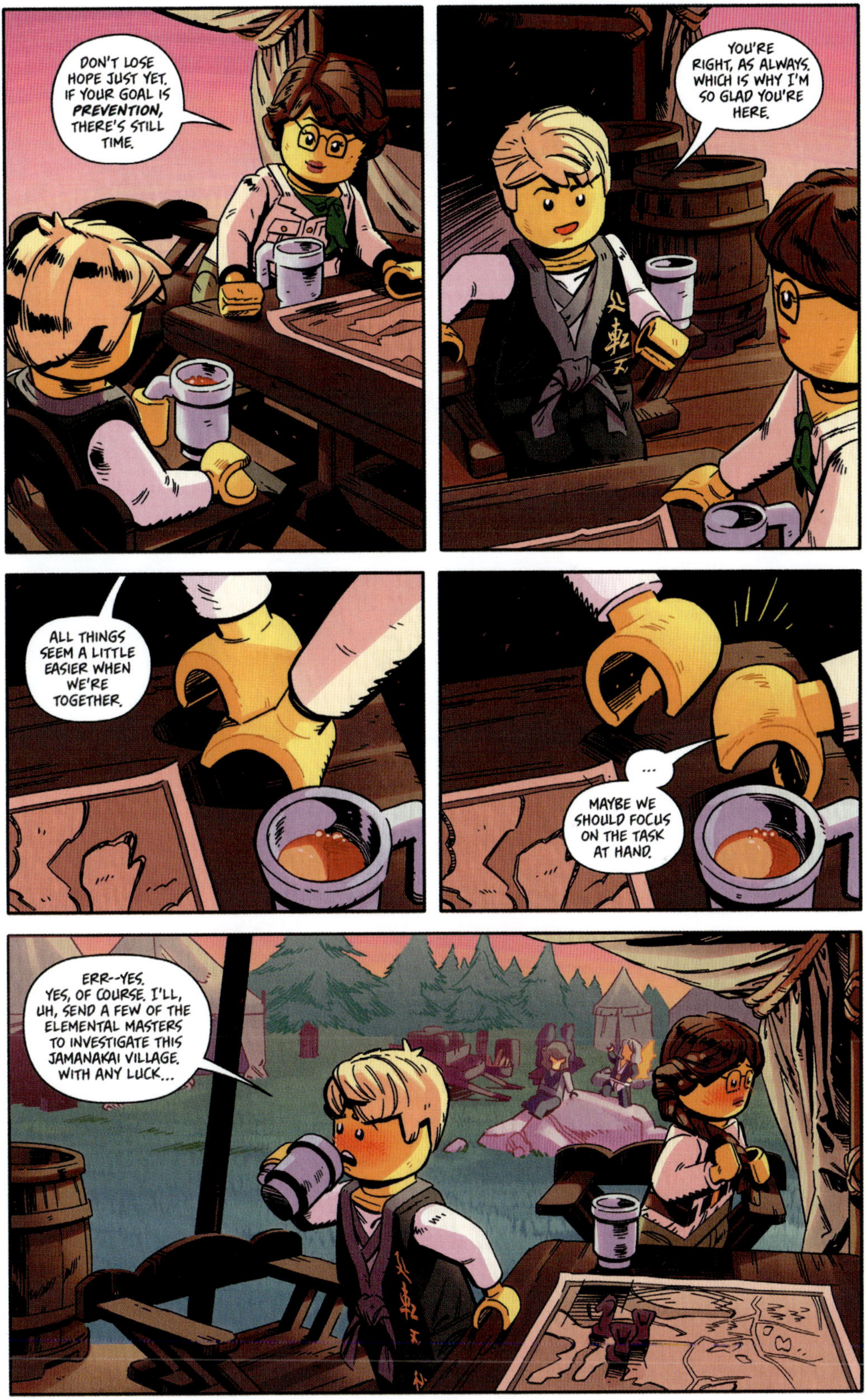
DON'T LOSE HOPE JUST YET. IF YOUR GOAL IS **PREVENTION**, THERE'S STILL TIME.
YOU'RE RIGHT, AS ALWAYS. WHICH IS WHY I'M SO GLAD YOU'RE HERE.
ALL THINGS SEEM A LITTLE EASIER WHEN WE'RE TOGETHER.
...
MAYBE WE SHOULD FOCUS ON THE TASK AT HAND.
ERR--YES. YES, OF COURSE. I'LL, UH, SEND A FEW OF THE ELEMENTAL MASTERS TO INVESTIGATE THIS JAMANAKAI VILLAGE. WITH ANY LUCK...

"...THERE'S NOTHING TO SEE."
YOU CAN'T HIDE THEM FROM US FOREVER!
GIVE US BACK OUR ARTIFACTS!
RETURN WHAT'S RIGHTFULLY OURSSSS!
W-WE DON'T KNOW WHAT YOU'RE TALKING ABOUT!
LOOK AROUND-- WE DON'T HAVE ANY RARE VALUABLES!
DON'T BOTHER LYING, OR WE'LL HAVE TO CHANGE YOUR MINDS.
OR MAYBE WE'LL SQUEEZE THE INFORMATION OUT OF YOU.

ENOUGH!
SPLAT
GAH!
I'VE BEEN HIT! THOSE MONSTERS ATTACKED ME!
OHHH, THE INDIGNITY!
ARE WE DONE ASKING NICELY?
OH, YESSSSS.

ATTACK!
JUST AS MASTER CHEN PLANNED...
...IT FINALLY BEGINS.

THEY WON'T GIVE US WHAT WE WANT, SO TAKE EVERYTHING!
NO NEED FOR TORCHES, FELLAS...

...I CAN BRING THE HEAT.

I-I CAN'T BELIEVE IT. IT'S CHAOS.
YOU DON'T SAY! THE HUMANS AREN'T BOWING DOWN TO OUR DEMANDS?
THEY TURNED IT INTO A...A BATTLE.
DON'T FRET. A SWATH OF RAGGEDY VILLAGERS DON'T STAND A CHANCE AGAINST THE LIKES OF THE SERPENTINE.
"THEY'RE NOT ALONE. THEY HAVE...POWERFUL BEINGS AMONG THEM."
THEY LOOK UNSTOPPABLE.
UNSTOPPABLE, YOU SAY?

WE WILL BE THE JUDGE OF THAT.
GENERAL ARCTURUS, IF YOU GO, YOU HAVE TO TRY AND RESTORE THE PEACE! WE WANT THEM TO FEAR THE PROPHECY, NOT US.
GENERAL, PLEASE!
WELL, I MUST HAND IT TO YOU, STRIKE, YOU WERE RIGHT AFTER ALL...
...THE ANACONDRAI DID JOIN IN ON THE FESTIVITIES. NOW ALL THE TRIBES ARE TOGETHER IN THE HAPPY FAMILY REUNION YOU ALWAYS DREAMED OF.
AHAHAH!

SAFE TO SAY WU WAS RIGHT--
--THE SERPENTINE WERE BEHIND THE ATTACKS.
DUSK IS RIGHT.
AND IF WE'RE LUCKY, WE CAN PUT A QUICK END TO ALL THIS!
WELL, HOPEFULLY NOT TOO QUICKLY, RIGHT, MAYA?
THAT'S RIGHT, RAY. I WOULDN'T MIND HAVING JUST A LITTLE BIT OF FUN.
YOUR FUN ENDS NOW, HUMANS.

ANACONDRAI WARRIORS--
LET THEM HAVE IT!

OKAY, I CAN CONFIRM--THIS IS NOT AS FUN!
DON'T WORRY, WE'LL BE PUT OUT OF OUR MISERY SOON IF WE DON'T COME UP WITH A BETTER PLAN.
THE ONLY GOOD PLAN I SEE? WE START WORKING TOGETHER.
YEAH? TELL THAT TO THE MASTER OF GRAVITY!
DID HE FLEE?
NO...
...HE'S HEADED FOR THE BELLY OF THE BEAST.

HELP!!
PLEASE!
BENTON! LEO! DO EITHER OF YOU KNOW WHAT'S HAPPENED?!
LOOK AT THEM, HIBERNUS--WHAT DO YOU THINK HAPPENED?!
IS THAT...A SNAKE?!
WE'RE MORE WORRIED ABOUT WHO'S INSIDE.
...INSIDE?

LEVI?!
SOUNDS LIKE HE'LL MAKE IT.
KAFF KAFF
NOT A GREAT PLACE TO BE FOUND. BUT THANK YOU.
WE THOUGHT WE LOST YOU.

POINT ME IN THE DIRECTION OF THESE SNAKES, AND I'LL TAKE CARE OF THE REST.
WE DON'T KNOW WHAT HAPPENED.
WHAT BECAME OF THE VILLAGE, AND THE VILLAGERS?
THE ANACONDRAI SHOWED NO MERCY.
THESE WARRIORS ARE NOT NORMAL SERPENTINE. THEY'RE STRONGER. MORE CUNNING.
NOT TO BE TRIFLED OR REASONED WITH.
THEY CAME PREPARED, WU.
THEY CAME FOR BATTLE! WE'RE THE ONES WHO CHOSE TO PRETEND OTHERWISE, AND NOW LIVES HAVE BEEN LOST.
WHAT OTHER SIGNS DO YOU ALL NEED BEFORE YOU WAKE UP?!

THWAK!
NICE TRY--
--BROTHER. BUT STEALTH WAS NEVER YOUR FORTE.
HEH. IT'S OVERRATED IN MY OPINION.
I WISH I CAME DURING HAPPIER TIMES, NOT AS NINJAGO PLUNGES INTO BATTLE.
YES, BUT, GARMADON, WITH THE TWO OF US FIGHTING SIDE-BY-SIDE, WE MIGHT BE ABLE TO WIN!
I WISH I SHARED YOUR CONFIDENCE.
HERE, SIT WITH ME. THERE'S MUCH TO DISCUSS.

YOU REALLY DON'T SEE A PATH TO VICTORY?
AS THINGS STAND? NO.
"AS WE SPEAK, THEIR FORCES ARE RALLYING FOR ANOTHER ATTACK.
"IF WE'RE TO HAVE ANY CHANCE, WE NEED POWER.
"I KNOW I'VE BEEN AWAY, BUT I WAS TRAINING. MY FORMER MASTER GAVE ME A PARTING GIFT...
"...AND I KNOW IT WILL UNLOCK GREAT THINGS."

WHERE WILL THIS "POWER" COME FROM?
I'M SORRY-- THERE'S MUCH I CAN'T TELL YOU, BUT I HOPE TO SHOW YOU ONCE I RETURN.
I HAVE FAITH IN YOU, GARMADON, BUT WE SHOULD BE TAKING ON THIS CHALLENGE TOGETHER. INSTEAD...
"...I FIND MYSELF ALONE, FACED WITH THE REALITY THAT THERE'S NO TURNING BACK."
THE MASTER OF EARTH IS RIGHT. THE SERPENTINE HAVE CHOSEN A FIGHT, AND DESPITE MY HOPES, WE HAVE NO CHOICE BUT TO MEET THEM.
ALONE, IF WE HAVE TO.
I WILL BE BACK. I PROMISE.

IF YOU SEE MISAKO BEFORE I RETURN, TELL HER--
NO.
WHEN YOU COME BACK SAFELY, YOU CAN TELL HER IN YOUR OWN WORDS.
RIGHT. OF COURSE.
BE SAFE, BROTHER.
WE WILL DO WHAT WE CAN HERE...
"...NO MATTER WHAT COMES OUR WAY."

CHAPTER 3
FAR AND WIDE

SUNBREAK VALLEY, NINJAGO ISLAND.
MANY SKIRMISHES AFTER THE BATTLE OF JAMANAKAI VILLAGE.
THANK YOU AGAIN FOR YOUR HELP, MISAKO. IT'S BEEN WEEKS SINCE OUR FOOD STORES HAVE BEEN REPLENISHED.
FINDING NEW DELIVERY ROUTES IS THE LEAST I CAN DO.
YES, WELL, IT FEELS MUCH BIGGER THAN THAT.
HAVE YOU HEARD ANYTHING FROM THE FRONTLINES? ANY HOPE THIS WAR WILL BE OVER SOON?
I CAN'T KNOW FOR SURE. BUT THERE'S ONE THING I DO KNOW.

BATTLE OF HEADSTONE ROAD.
"ALL ACROSS NINJAGO.
"...HEROES ARE RISING TO THE OCCASION.

BATTLE OF TANAKA CITY.
"IF YOU FEEL ISOLATED IN YOUR VILLAGE,
"...KNOW THAT THESE WARRIORS ARE WORKING TOGETHER ON BEHALF OF *EVERY* CITIZEN OF NINJAGO...
"...FOR THE SAKE OF YOUR PAST AND FUTURE ALIKE.

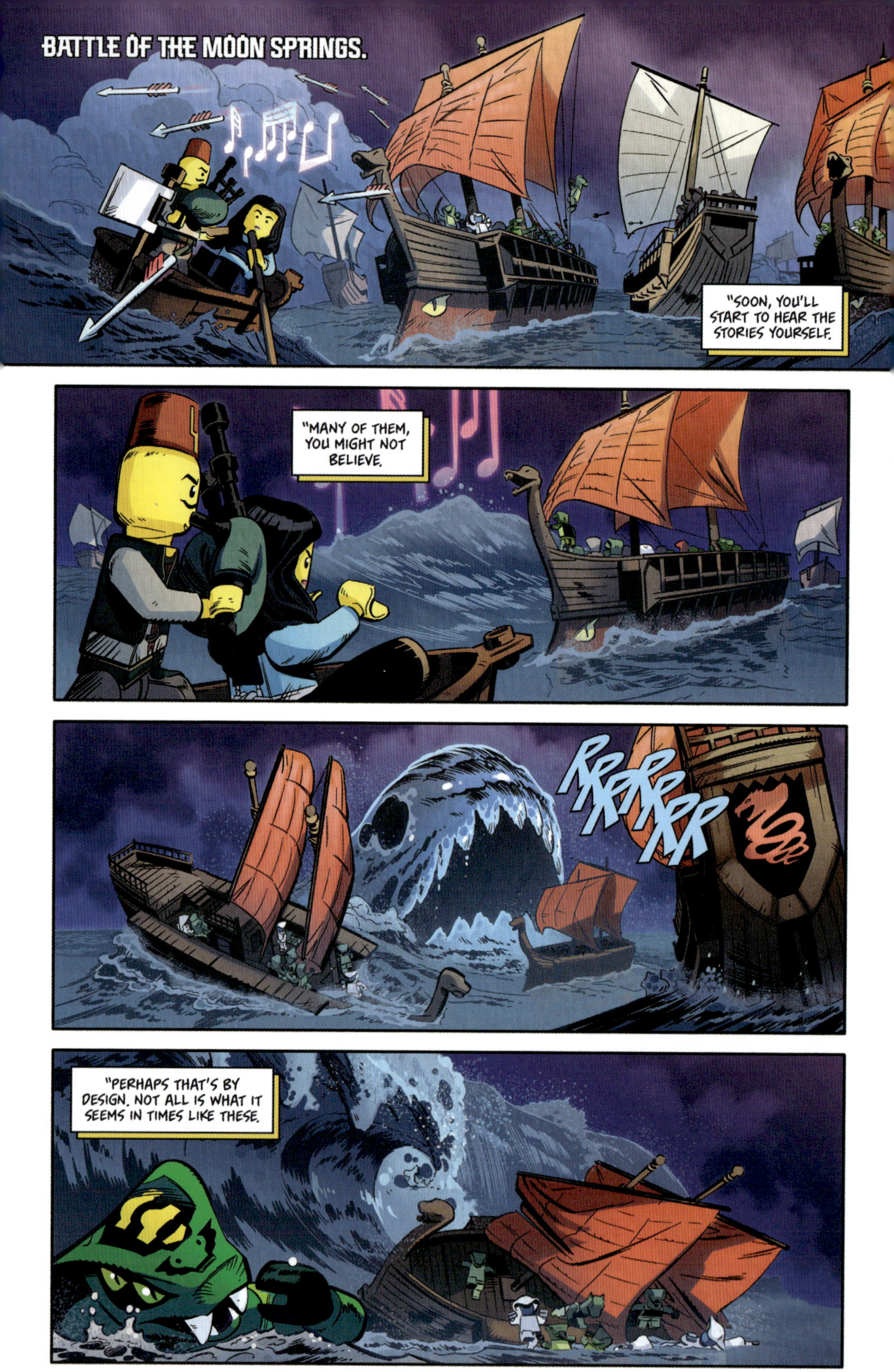
BATTLE OF THE MOON SPRINGS.
"SOON, YOU'LL START TO HEAR THE STORIES YOURSELF.
"MANY OF THEM, YOU MIGHT NOT BELIEVE.
RRRRRRR
"PERHAPS THAT'S BY DESIGN. NOT ALL IS WHAT IT SEEMS IN TIMES LIKE THESE.

BATTLE OF BLACK CLIFFS.
"BUT EVEN WITH ALL THE VALOR AND COURAGE.
"...IT MAY NOT BE ENOUGH.
"YOU WILL NOT SEE ME LOSE HOPE YET, BUT...
"I FEAR THIS WAR IS STILL FAR FROM OVER."

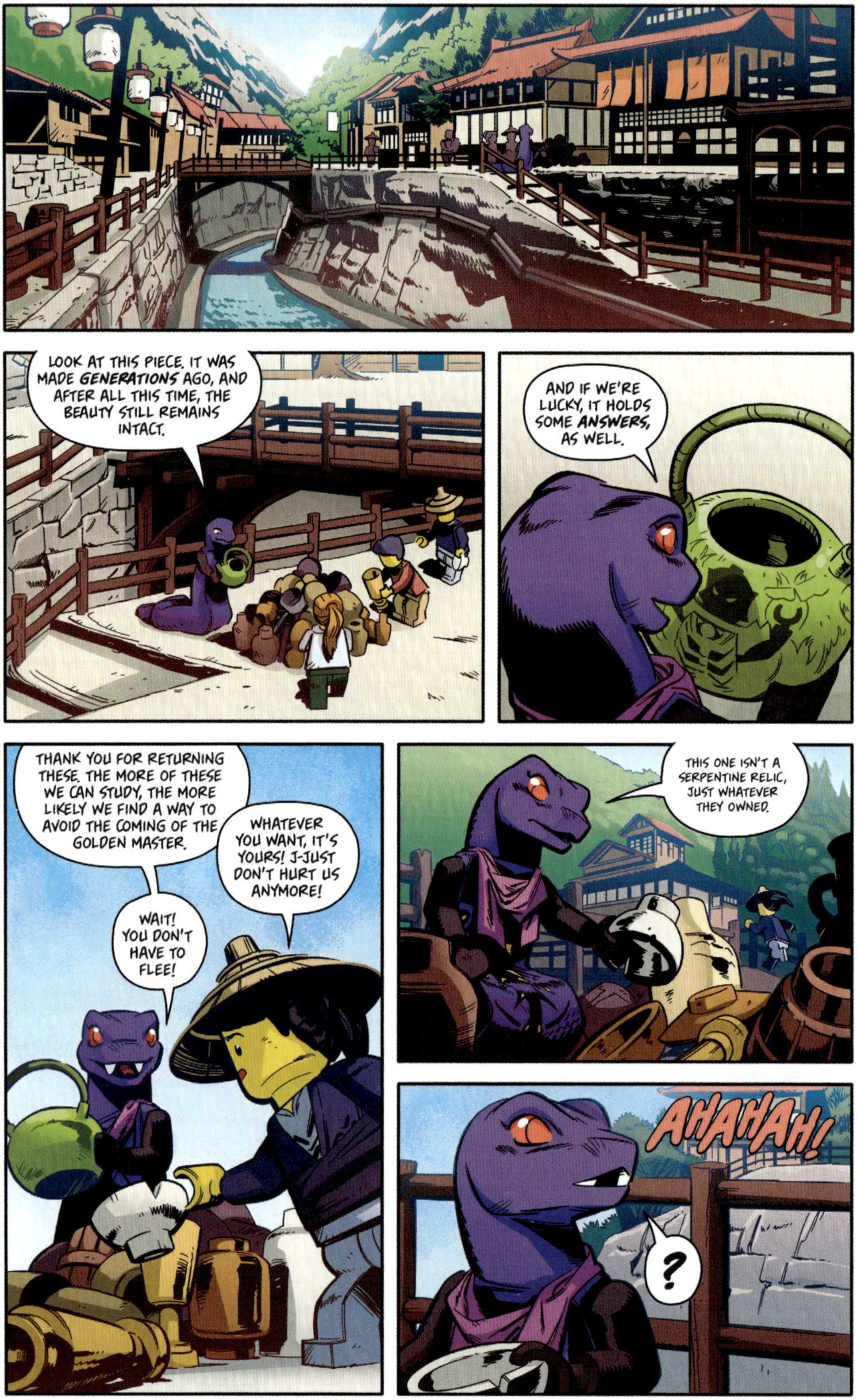
LOOK AT THIS PIECE. IT WAS MADE GENERATIONS AGO, AND AFTER ALL THIS TIME, THE BEAUTY STILL REMAINS INTACT.
AND IF WE'RE LUCKY, IT HOLDS SOME ANSWERS, AS WELL.
THANK YOU FOR RETURNING THESE. THE MORE OF THESE WE CAN STUDY, THE MORE LIKELY WE FIND A WAY TO AVOID THE COMING OF THE GOLDEN MASTER.
WHATEVER YOU WANT, IT'S YOURS! J-JUST DON'T HURT US ANYMORE!
WAIT! YOU DON'T HAVE TO FLEE!
THIS ONE ISN'T A SERPENTINE RELIC, JUST WHATEVER THEY OWNED.
AHAHAH!
?

AND THE TERROR ON THEIR FACES WHEN YOU REPELLED UPON THEM. IT WAS DELICIOUS.
AHAHAH!
MAKE NO MISTAKE, WE MADE GREAT GAINS DURING THIS BATTLE.
IF I MAY ASK...GAINS TOWARDS WHAT EXACTLY?
I THOUGHT ALL OF THIS WAS TO PREVENT THE PROPHECY OF THE GOLDEN MASTER. HAVE YOU INSPECTED OUR LATEST DISCOVERIES FOR NEW INSIGHTS?
WE MOST CERTAINLY DID. THE ONE YOU'RE HOLDING HAPPENS TO BE MY PERSONAL FAVORITE OF THE SET.
IT'S A BOWL. MADE BY A HUMAN.

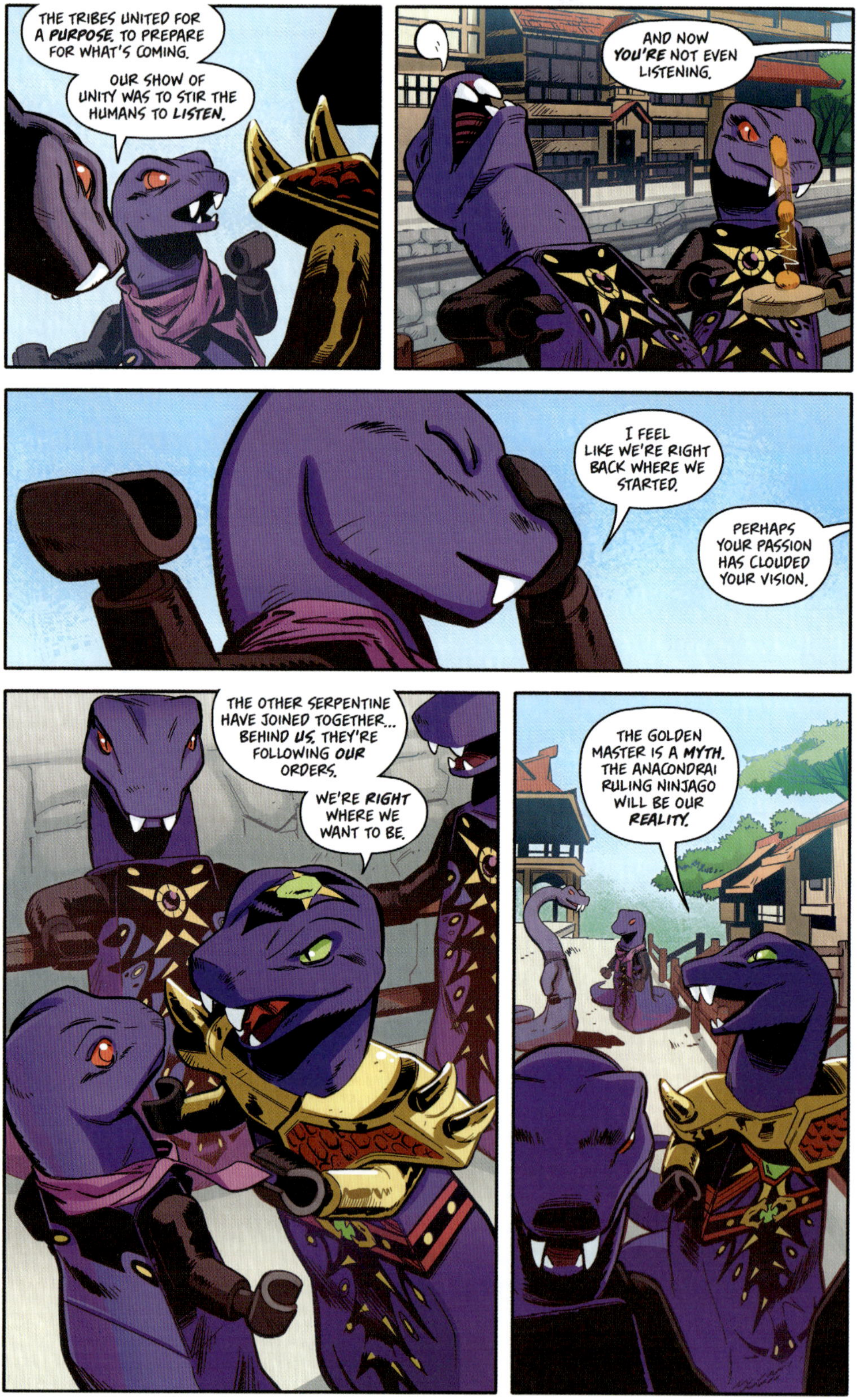
THE TRIBES UNITED FOR A PURPOSE. TO PREPARE FOR WHAT'S COMING.
OUR SHOW OF UNITY WAS TO STIR THE HUMANS TO LISTEN.
AND NOW YOU'RE NOT EVEN LISTENING.
I FEEL LIKE WE'RE RIGHT BACK WHERE WE STARTED.
PERHAPS YOUR PASSION HAS CLOUDED YOUR VISION.
THE OTHER SERPENTINE HAVE JOINED TOGETHER... BEHIND US. THEY'RE FOLLOWING OUR ORDERS.
WE'RE RIGHT WHERE WE WANT TO BE.
THE GOLDEN MASTER IS A MYTH. THE ANACONDRAI RULING NINJAGO WILL BE OUR REALITY.

SORRY, DEAR. UNITY OR NOT, *HE'S* THE *BOSS.*
WHOSE SIDE ARE YOU EVEN *ON,* PYTHOR?
COME NOW, ISN'T IT *OBVIOUS?*
I'M ON MY *OWN* SIDE.
HE'S A BIT OF A CHARACTER, ISN'T HE?
CHEN?! WHAT ARE YOU DOING HERE? IF GENERAL ARCTURUS SEES A *HUMAN* HERE--
PLEASE, CALL ME *MASTER* CHEN. AND DON'T WORRY, THE GENERAL AND I MET RECENTLY. WE'RE PRACTICALLY OLD FRIENDS NOW.
HE AND I SHARE THE DESIRE FOR A SERPENTINE *VICTORY.* I CAN *PROVE* IT TO YOU.
COME, COME, STRIKE...

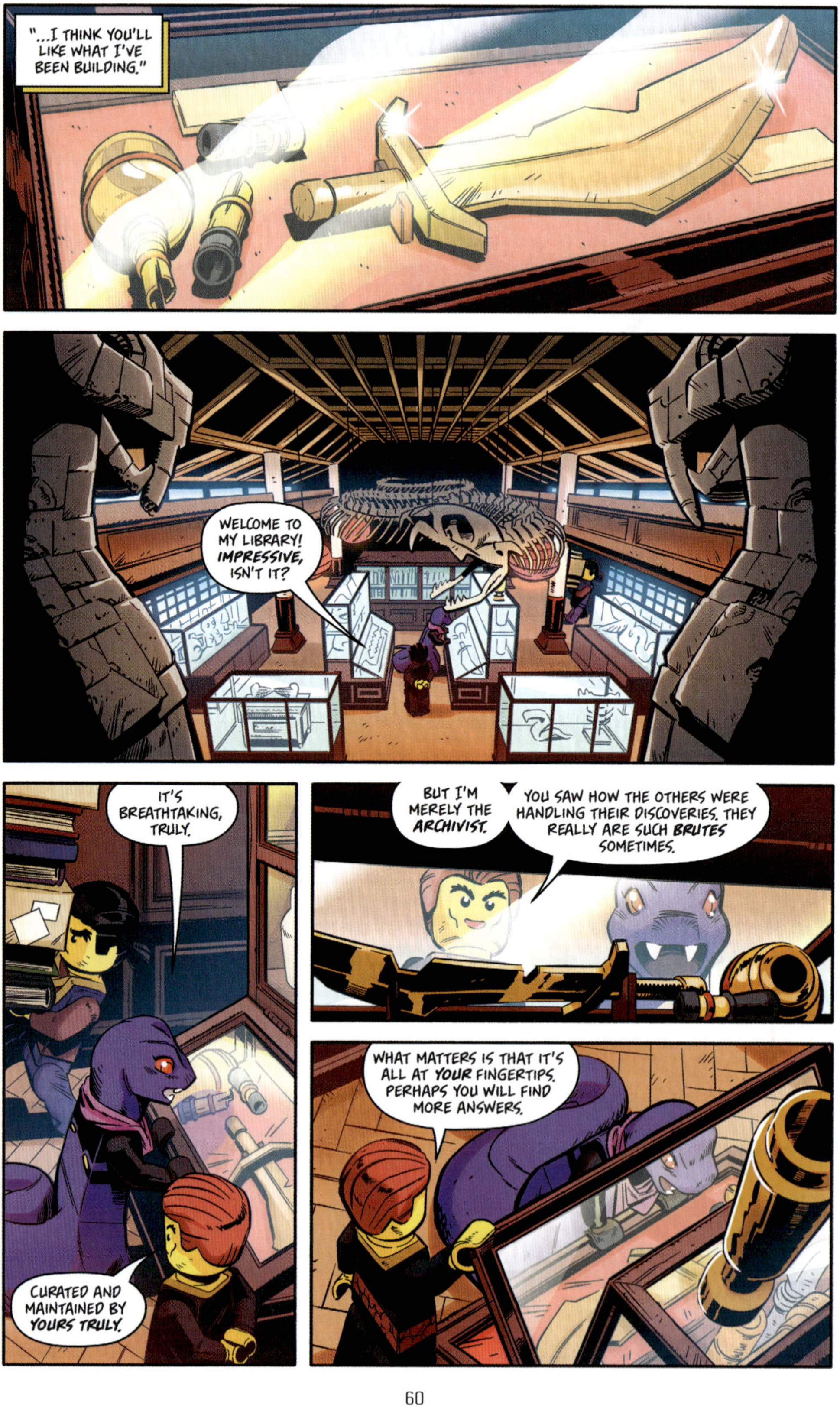
"...I THINK YOU'LL LIKE WHAT I'VE BEEN BUILDING."
WELCOME TO MY LIBRARY! IMPRESSIVE, ISN'T IT?
IT'S BREATHTAKING, TRULY.
CURATED AND MAINTAINED BY YOURS TRULY.
BUT I'M MERELY THE ARCHIVIST.
YOU SAW HOW THE OTHERS WERE HANDLING THEIR DISCOVERIES. THEY REALLY ARE SUCH BRUTES SOMETIMES.
WHAT MATTERS IS THAT IT'S ALL AT YOUR FINGERTIPS. PERHAPS YOU WILL FIND MORE ANSWERS.

MAYBE THERE IS NO ESCAPING THE PROPHECY. THE MORE I TRY TO FEND OFF ITS ARRIVAL, THE CLOSER IT SEEMS TO COME.
YES, WELL, IT WILL BE EVEN CLOSER IF YOU GIVE UP.
THIS COLLECTION IS A CHANCE, A RARE CHANCE, TO UNLOCK THE TRUTH! DON'T WASTE IT.
DO YOU HAVE PIECES FROM THE OTHER TRIBES? I ONLY SEE ANACONDRAI.
HM? OH, I TEND TO FOCUS ON THE ANACONDRAI. THEY'RE THE WARRIORS! SURELY THOSE ARE THE ANSWERS WORTH FINDING.
IT IS A WAR, AFTER ALL.

WHY ALL THE LONG FACES?
I TAKE IT YOU'RE NOT THE MASTER OF OBSERVATION, BENTON? WE'RE GETTING CLOBBERED OUT THERE!
AND OUR NUMBERS ARE DWINDLING. KRUX AND ACRONIX FOUGHT BRAVELY, BUT WHEN THE DUST CLEARED FROM THE BATTLE, THERE WAS NO SIGN OF THEM.
ALL THE MORE REASON NOT TO GIVE UP. WHERE'S YOUR WARRIOR SPIRIT?!
THE SNAKES TOOK IT, AND I DON'T THINK THEY'RE GIVING IT BACK.
THEY HAVEN'T EVEN RETURNED THE MASTER OF FORM.
THE MASTER OF FORM WAS CAPTURED?!
WHO KNOWS WHERE HE IS NOW.
I DO.

ANACONDRAI!
NOT ANOTHER STEP, YOU **MONSTER!**
TELL US WHERE OUR ALLY IS, OR YOU'LL SPEND THE REST OF YOUR DAYS AS A **STATUE.**
THE ANSWER TO **THAT**--
--IS RIGHT IN FRONT OF YOU.
MASTER OF FORM! YOU'RE ALL RIGHT!
YOU COULDN'T HAVE JUST SHOWN UP AS YOURSELF?
I **COULD** HAVE, BUT THEN WHERE'S THE **DRAMA?**
"WHEN OUR CHANCES AT THE BATTLE OF BLACK CLIFFS SEEMED **DOOMED**, I THOUGHT I MIGHT TRY TO GET **SOMETHING** OUT OF OUR EFFORTS."
DID IT WORK? DID YOU GET ANYTHING WE CAN USE?
OH, I'D SAY THEY BOUGHT MY PERFORMANCE. AND NOW...

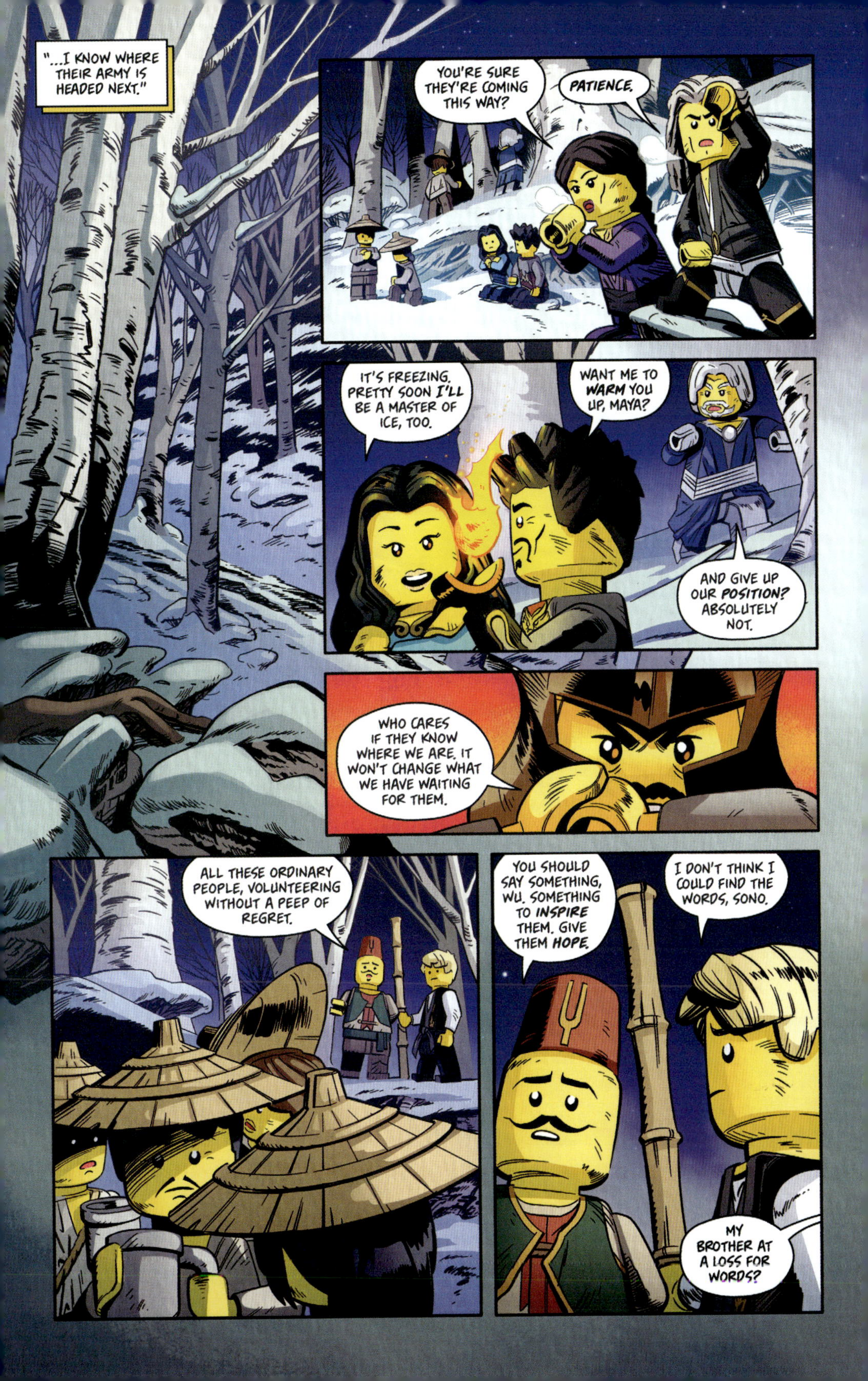
"...I KNOW WHERE THEIR ARMY IS HEADED NEXT."
YOU'RE SURE THEY'RE COMING THIS WAY?
PATIENCE.
IT'S FREEZING. PRETTY SOON I'LL BE A MASTER OF ICE, TOO.
WANT ME TO WARM YOU UP, MAYA?
AND GIVE UP OUR POSITION? ABSOLUTELY NOT.
WHO CARES IF THEY KNOW WHERE WE ARE. IT WON'T CHANGE WHAT WE HAVE WAITING FOR THEM.
ALL THESE ORDINARY PEOPLE, VOLUNTEERING WITHOUT A PEEP OF REGRET.
YOU SHOULD SAY SOMETHING, WU. SOMETHING TO INSPIRE THEM. GIVE THEM HOPE.
I DON'T THINK I COULD FIND THE WORDS, SONO.
MY BROTHER AT A LOSS FOR WORDS?

I NEVER THOUGHT I'D SEE THE DAY.
GARMADON! YOU'VE RETURNED!
DID YOU FIND WHAT YOU WERE LOOKING FOR?
I WISH I CAME BEARING BETTER NEWS, BROTHER, BUT MY QUEST PROVED TO BE A DECEPTION FROM MY FORMER MASTER.
"I FOUND... NOTHING FOR US."*
*AS TOLD IN LEGO NINJAGO: SHATTERSPIN!

I KNOW HOW MUCH NINJAGO HAS ENDURED IN MY ABSENCE. I'M SORRY I LEFT YOU ALL *EXPOSED.*
YOU ARE HERE NOW. *THAT* IS WHAT MATTERS.
YOUR ALLIANCE SEEMS TO HAVE STRENGTHENED IN MY TIME AWAY. THEY'VE BECOME AN IMPRESSIVE FORCE.
BAROOOOM
BAROOOOM
TIME TO PUT THAT TO THE TEST.

THE FAMED SPINJITZU BROTHERS. THIS IS A PLEASANT SURPRISE.
THERE'S NOTHING PLEASANT ABOUT ANY OF THIS, GENERAL ARCTURUS.
TRUST ME--DESTROYING BOTH OF YOU AT ONCE WILL BE.
UNLESS YOU'D RATHER SET DOWN YOUR ARMS AND SURRENDER ALL OF NINJAGO TO THE SERPENTINE?
I HAVE LONG WISHED THERE WAS ANOTHER WAY, BUT IT'S COME TO THIS.

SHOW NO MERCY!
WAIT FOR IT...
I THINK I'VE WAITED LONG ENOUGH!
FOR THE SERPENTINE!
HEH! ELEMENTAL MASTERS! WHERE'S OUR BATTLE CRY?
WILL THUNDER DO?
ONLY IF THE LIGHTNING GIVES ME A PROPER SPOTLIGHT!
YOU TAKE ALL THEIR ATTENTION AND THEY WON'T SEE ME COMING.
NOW THAT WE'RE NOT FIGHTING ALONE...
...THIS IS KIND OF FUN!
FIIIIIRE!
SPEAK FOR YOURSELF!
I'LL LET MY MELODY DO THE TALKING.
NO MATTER WHAT POWER RESIDES IN YOUR SOUND...

"...IT'S NOTHING COMPARED TO THE SOUND OF BATTLE!"

WHO'S NEXT?! I'M NOT EVEN BREAKING A SWEAT!
MY TURN.
I THINK YOU'LL DO JUST FINE.
THIS IS FOR THE PEOPLE OF NINJAGO. FOR GLORY. FOR--
--!?

IT'S TIME TO FACE THE FACTS, ARCTURUS! WITH ALL OF US WORKING SIDE BY SIDE--
--YOU NEVER STOOD A CHANCE.
YOU'RE SURE YOU'RE **ALL** ON THE SAME SIDE?
!

GAH!!
WELL?
WHO'S NEXT?!

CHAPTER 4
BETRAYAL

RETREAT!

THAT'S ALL YOU'VE GOT?! COME BACK SO I CAN GROUND YOU INTO DUST!
SPOKEN WITH THE FURY OF A TRUE ANACONDRAI.
HEHEH!
I'M SURPRISED I DON'T SEE A TAIL SPROUTING OUT OF HIS BACK.
HAHAH!
THAT'S NOT A BAD IDEA, BUT I BELIEVE ONE SPELL WAS SUFFICIENT.
FAREWELL, ELEMENTAL MASTER.
"YOUR FIGHTING PROWESS DID NOT DISAPPOINT."
WH-WHERE AM I?
NO.
NO, NO, NO...

WHAT HAVE I DONE?
WHAT EVERY WARRIOR HOPES TO DO...
YOU MONSTER. I'LL--
...PROVE YOUR WORTH.
I DON'T THINK YOUR FRIENDS WOULD CONSIDER ME THE MONSTER. NOT AFTER WHAT YOU'VE DONE HERE.

WHAT HAPPENED BACK THERE, BROTHER?! YOUR OWN ALLIANCE MEMBER, HE--
I KNOW. BUT...I CAN'T BRING MYSELF TO BELIEVE IT.
ASSUMING WE CAN TRUST THE OTHERS--
WE CAN. SOMETHING ELSE IS AT WORK, I'M SURE OF IT. WE CANNOT LOSE FAITH NOW.
"ALL WE NEED IS A PLACE TO REST AND REGROUP."
JAMANAKAI VILLAGE.
WE LOST OUR BATTLE HERE. WE'RE SURE THE ANACONDRAI AREN'T STILL LYING IN WAIT?
THERE AREN'T MANY PLACES LEFT WHERE THE ANACONDRAI AREN'T IN CONTROL. LET'S BE THANKFUL THEY'VE LOST INTEREST IN THIS ONE.
?

REMARKABLE, ISN'T IT? THE WAY THE FLUTE'S PITCH CAPTURES THE SNAKE? I CAN'T SAY I BLAME THE LITTLE ONE--IT'S A LOVELY TUNE.
YES. IF ONLY OUR PROBLEMS COULD BE SOLVED SO EASILY.

YOU MIGHT BE CLOSER TO THE TRUTH THAN YOU REALIZE.
UH, LEO? IS THAT YOU AGAIN?
NO, BUT THEY DO HAVE IMPECCABLE TIMING.
SO, IT'S AN ENEMY AMBUSH THEN?
I'M ALONE AND HERE TO HELP.
IT'S NOT AN AMBUSH. NOR A TRICK. THOUGH...

"...I BELIEVE THAT'S WHAT HAPPENED TO YOUR FRIEND."
YOU.

YOU SAW ALL THAT AND CAME HERE TO TEASE ME, DIDN'T YOU, BROOK? TO TELL ME YOU WERE RIGHT?
NO NEED TO TELL ME WHAT I ALREADY KNOW. WHAT WILL HAUNT ME FOR THE REST OF MY DAYS.
I'VE SEEN SO MUCH SINCE WE LAST MET. THE WORLD IS SCARRED AND BREAKING.
I'M HERE BECAUSE DESPITE ALL THAT...
...I STILL BELIEVE THINGS CAN GROW ANEW.

WHAT DO YOU THINK, BROTHER? ARE WE FALLING FOR A TRAP?
YOU KNOW WHAT THE ANACONDRAI ARE CAPABLE OF.
TREACHERY.
VIOLENCE.
POOR SKIN CARE.
...
WHAT? YOU TRY SHEDDING YOUR SKIN AND SEE HOW YOU LIKE IT!
IF WE'RE LUCKY, THAT LIST INCLUDES SURPRISES.
MY NAME IS WU. AND YOU ARE?
STRIKE.
COME, LET ME INTRODUCE YOU TO MY FRIENDS. IF WE GIVE EACH OTHER A CHANCE...

"...PERHAPS THERE'S MUCH WE CAN LEARN FROM EACH OTHER."
THE FIRST THING TO KNOW, STRIKE, IS THAT WE HAVE BEEN THROUGH A LOT.
FORGIVE US IF WE'RE ON EDGE.
OF ALL THE SENSELESS BATTLES WE'VE FOUGHT, IT'S BEING ATTACKED BY ONE OF OUR OWN THAT HAUNTS US THE MOST.
SO. PLEASE, IF YOU CAN...
HELP US UNDERSTAND.
I...
I WANTED TO SEE THE SERPENTINE WORKING TOGETHER. JUST ONCE.

"THERE WAS NO LACK OF STORIES COMING FROM THE FRONTLINES, BUT I WANTED TO SEE FOR MYSELF.
"I EXPECTED TO SEE THE VALOR OF OUR UNIFIED FORCES AND THE RUTHLESSNESS OF OUR ENEMIES.
"INSTEAD, I SAW THE ANACONDRAI ON THEIR OWN...
"...AND YOU ALL WORKING TOGETHER.
"BUT...I ALSO SAW A THIRD PLAYER, WIELDING SOMETHING FROM THE SHADOWS.
"A DARK AND POWERFUL MAGIC.

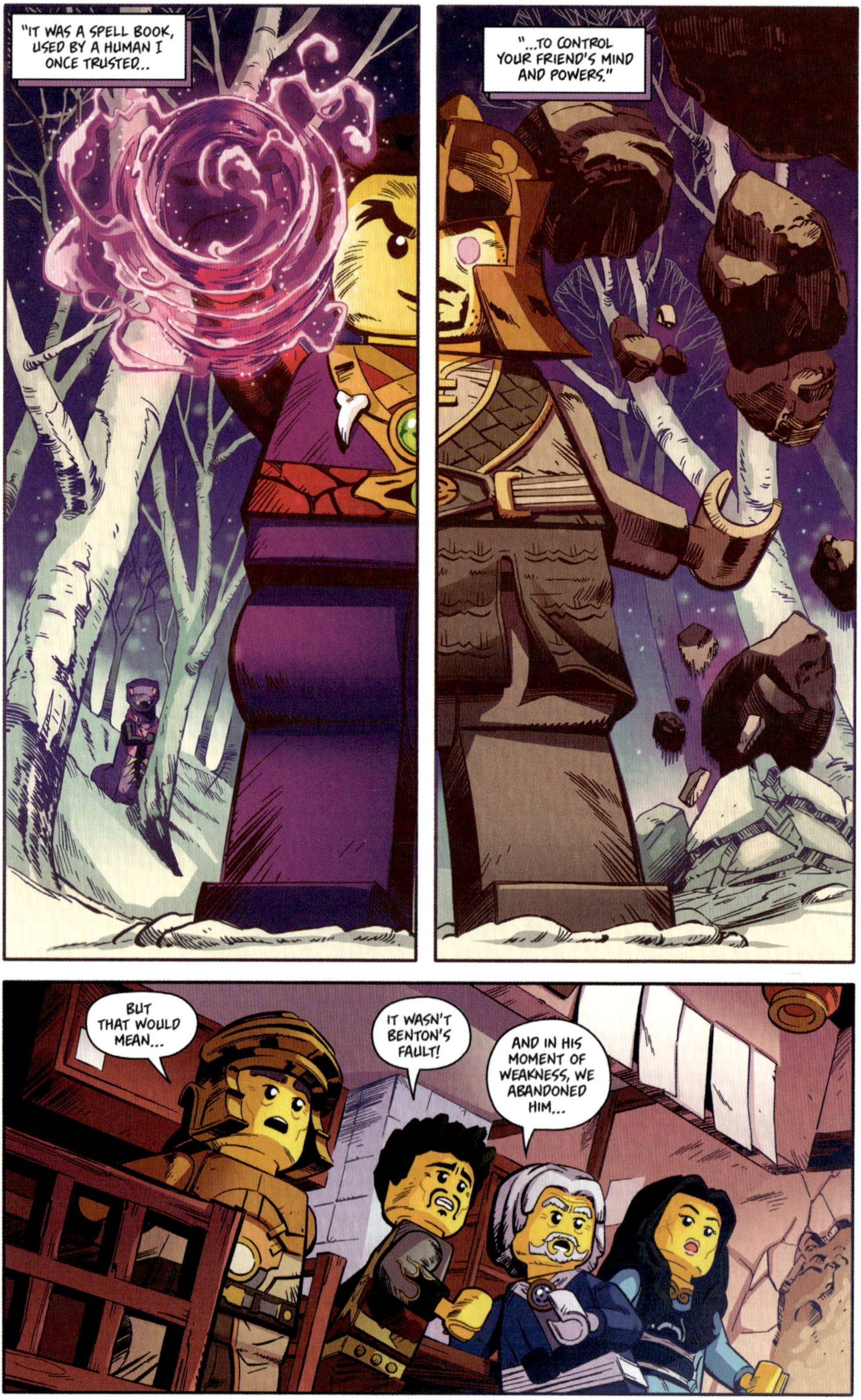
"IT WAS A SPELL BOOK, USED BY A HUMAN I ONCE TRUSTED...
"...TO CONTROL YOUR FRIEND'S MIND AND POWERS."
BUT THAT WOULD MEAN...
IT WASN'T BENTON'S FAULT!
AND IN HIS MOMENT OF WEAKNESS, WE ABANDONED HIM...

I'M SORRY IF HEARING THIS MAKES THINGS MORE DIFFICULT.
NO, NO. I THINK YOUR STORY...HEALS MORE THAN HURTS.
BUT... MAY I ASK ANOTHER QUESTION? SINCE THIS ALL STARTED, I CAN'T GET IT OUT OF MY HEAD.
WE FORMED OUR ALLIANCE BECAUSE SERPENTINE FORCES WERE RAIDING VILLAGES, WEAKENING THEM BEFORE THE FIGHTING STARTED. BUT...
BUT WHAT? THAT SEEMS LIKE A LOGICAL MOVE IF THEY WERE PREPARING TO ATTACK.
YES, BUT, IF THEY WANTED THESE RAIDS TO BE DONE IN SECRET, THEY COULD HAVE BEEN.
"INSTEAD, WE HEARD DESCRIPTIONS OF THE WEAPONS USED. TALES OF 'HISSING' WARRIORS."
HSSSSS
AS IF THE SERPENTINE WANTED US TO KNOW IT WAS THEM.
EXACTLY. BUT WHY?

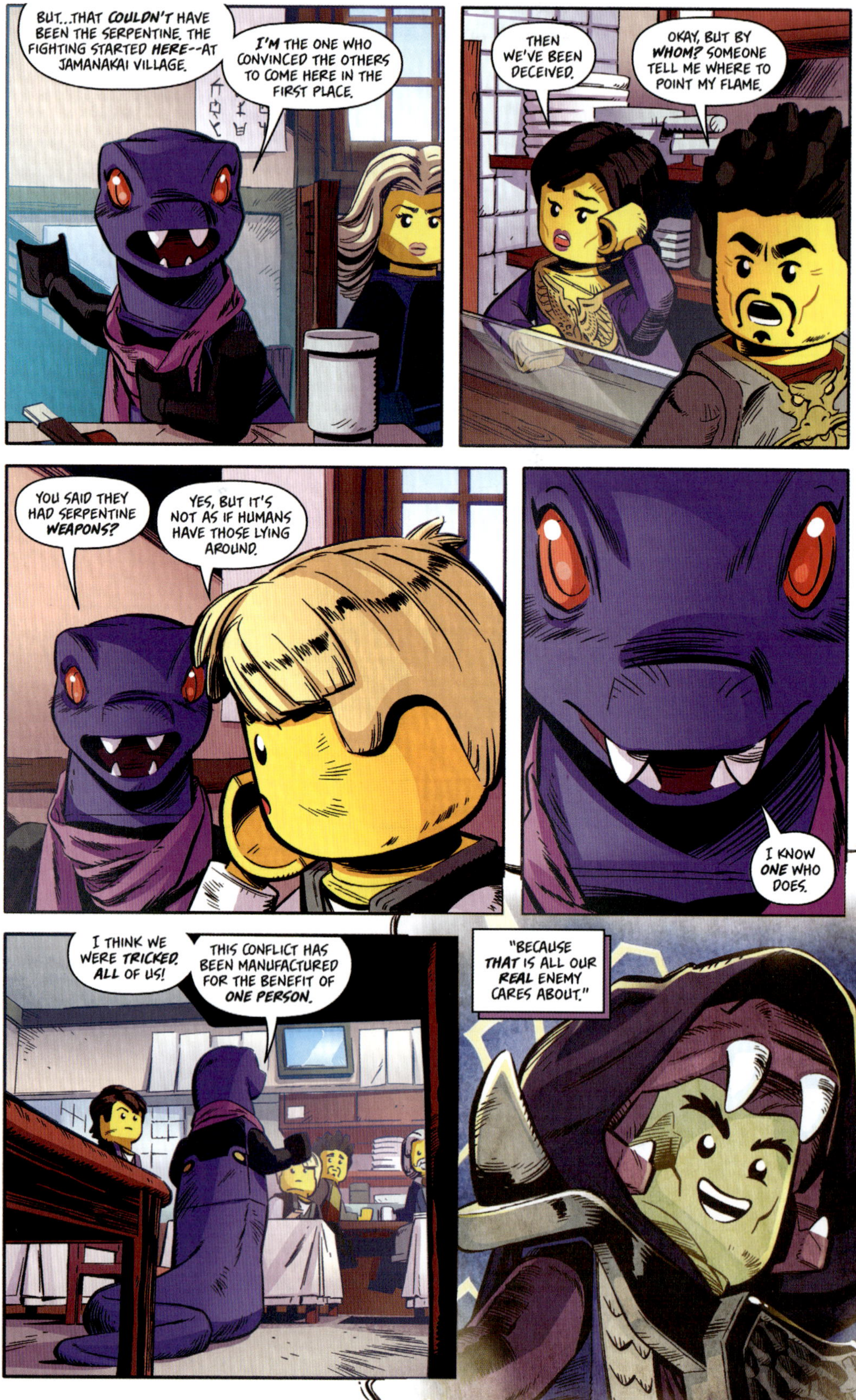

BUT...THAT COULDN'T HAVE BEEN THE SERPENTINE. THE FIGHTING STARTED HERE--AT JAMANAKAI VILLAGE.
I'M THE ONE WHO CONVINCED THE OTHERS TO COME HERE IN THE FIRST PLACE.
THEN WE'VE BEEN DECEIVED.
OKAY, BUT BY WHOM? SOMEONE TELL ME WHERE TO POINT MY FLAME.
YOU SAID THEY HAD SERPENTINE WEAPONS?
YES, BUT IT'S NOT AS IF HUMANS HAVE THOSE LYING AROUND.
I KNOW ONE WHO DOES.
I THINK WE WERE TRICKED. ALL OF US!
THIS CONFLICT HAS BEEN MANUFACTURED FOR THE BENEFIT OF ONE PERSON.
"BECAUSE THAT IS ALL OUR REAL ENEMY CARES ABOUT."

SO, YOU KNOW WHAT WE'RE UP AGAINST?
YES, AND TRUST ME...
...YOU'VE NEVER MET ANYONE LIKE MASTER CHEN AND HIS APPRENTICE.
THAT'S ALL WELL AND GOOD, BUT YOU MADE IT SOUND LIKE YOU HAD A WAY TO END THE WAR AND I'M STILL WAITING ON THE DETAILS.
YOU WERE THE ONE WHO PIECED IT TOGETHER. WHEN YOU NOTICED THE SNAKE CHARMER.
A SOUND I FOR ONE WON'T FORGET.
I WISH I COULD SAY THE SAME FOR THE SERPENTINE.

THE SERPENTINE ABANDONED JAMANAKAI VILLAGE AFTER THEIR VICTORY BECAUSE THEY DIDN'T SEE ANY **VALUE** IT MIGHT OFFER.
"THEY OBSESS OVER CONQUEST BUT FORGET OUR OWN HISTORY.
"LONG AGO, JAMANAKAI VILLAGE WAS A PLACE OF **HARMONY** FOR HUMANS AND THE SERPENTINE.

"SACRED FLUTES WERE USED TO CREATE PEACEFUL COMMUNICATION.
"FOR THE FIRST TIME, OUR DIFFERENCES WERE REPLACED BY TRULY UNDERSTANDING ONE ANOTHER.
"MEMORY FADED AND THE ACHIEVEMENT OF THIS VILLAGE WAS FORGOTTEN.
"IT SEEMS NOW THAT ANY CHANCE OF RETAINING THAT HARMONY IS *GONE...*"

BUT THE SACRED FLUTES **AREN'T.** AND I KNOW WHERE TO FIND THEM.
ALL THIS TIME, I'VE BEEN TRYING TO GET THE SERPENTINE TO LISTEN TO **EACH OTHER.** BUT NOW, THEY WON'T EVEN LISTEN TO **REASON.**
I **WISH** THERE WAS ANOTHER WAY, BUT THE FLUTES ARE THE ONLY WAY TO PROTECT HUMANS AND SERPENTINE ALIKE.
I ONCE HOPED THAT HARNESSING ENOUGH POWER--**FORCE**--WOULD BE THE ANSWER.
I WAS WRONG.
I THINK **LISTENING** AND WORKING WITH THOSE WHO WANT TO DO WHAT IS **RIGHT** IS THE MOST POWERFUL OPTION WE HAVE LEFT.
THEN WE'LL FIND THESE SACRED FLUTES. **TOGETHER.**
IF YOU'VE FOUND A WAY TO END ALL OF THIS...

WE WISH TO HELP.
IF YOU'LL HAVE US.
BENTON?! BROOK?!
I WORRIED I'D NEVER SEE EITHER OF YOU AGAIN, BUT CERTAINLY NOT *TOGETHER*.
TURNS OUT WE HAVE MORE IN COMMON THAN OUR POWERS--A DESIRE TO MAKE THINGS RIGHT.
I...I HOPE YOU CAN ALL FORGIVE ME. I DIDN'T...
WE KNOW.

IT APPEARS OUR ALLIANCE HAS GROWN, AND JUST IN TIME.
WE HAVE MADE MISTAKES AND COME UP SHORT. BUT WE ARE ALL STILL HERE FOR ONE REASON.
PEACE.
SO, UH, WHERE EXACTLY CAN WE FIND THESE ***FLUTES?*** I'M ANXIOUS TO GET MY HANDS ON THEM AND HEAR THEIR SONIC MAJESTY UP CLOSE!
I'M AFRAID IT WON'T BE EASY TO GET TO THEM...
"...BEHIND ENEMY LINES."

CHAPTER 5
BATTLE SONG

"I HAVE TO ADMIT, WU...WHEN YOU FIRST TOLD ME YOU WERE PUTTING TOGETHER AN ALLIANCE TO HELP SAVE NINJAGO..."
...FOLLOWING A SERPENTINE ISN'T EXACTLY WHAT I HAD IN MIND.
THAT GOES FOR BOTH OF US, SONO.
BRAVE WARRIORS FROM DIFFERENT BACKGROUNDS UNITING FOR A COMMON CAUSE...
THAT SOUNDS LIKE A TRUE ALLIANCE TO ME.
ONE I'M HONORED TO BE A PART OF, WU.
NOW, LET'S JUST HOPE OUR PLAN WORKS.

I'M HERE TO SEE GENERAL ARCTURUS!
WHAT FOR, STRIKE? MORE RABBLE ROUSING TO JEOPARDIZE OUR BATTLE PLANS?
YOUR PLANS, ARCTURUS? I DON'T THINK I NEED TO REMIND YOU WHOSE LIBRARY YOU'RE GUARDING.
HOLD YOUR TONGUE!
I THINK SHE'S PROVEN SHE CAN'T DO THAT.

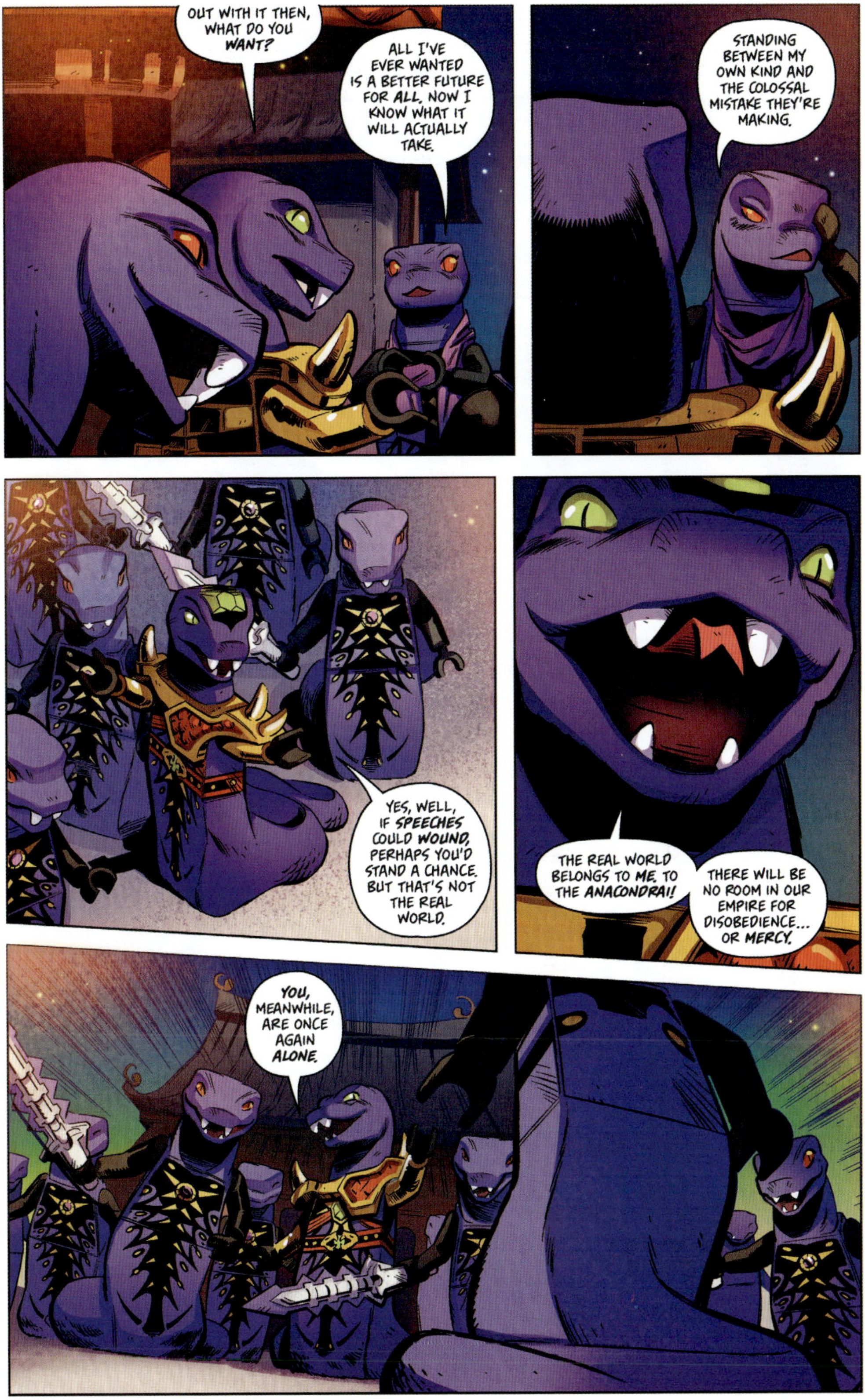
OUT WITH IT THEN, WHAT DO YOU WANT?
ALL I'VE EVER WANTED IS A BETTER FUTURE FOR ALL. NOW I KNOW WHAT IT WILL ACTUALLY TAKE.
STANDING BETWEEN MY OWN KIND AND THE COLOSSAL MISTAKE THEY'RE MAKING.
YES, WELL, IF SPEECHES COULD WOUND, PERHAPS YOU'D STAND A CHANCE. BUT THAT'S NOT THE REAL WORLD.
THE REAL WORLD BELONGS TO ME. TO THE ANACONDRAI!
THERE WILL BE NO ROOM IN OUR EMPIRE FOR DISOBEDIENCE... OR MERCY.
YOU, MEANWHILE, ARE ONCE AGAIN ALONE.

YOU SURE ABOUT THAT?

YOU THREE-- GET INSIDE! COMPLETE THE MISSION.
SONO CAN MAKE SURE THOSE FLUTES SING.
STRIKE KNOWS HOW TO FIND THEM.
AND BROOK CAN RECONSTRUCT THE WOODEN FRAMES.
WE'LL HOLD THE LINE.
WE ARE THE SONS OF THE FIRST **SPINJITZU MASTER.** WE WERE **BORN** FOR MOMENTS LIKE THESE!
WE'RE SIMPLY DOING OUR PART...

"...JUST LIKE EVERYONE ELSE."

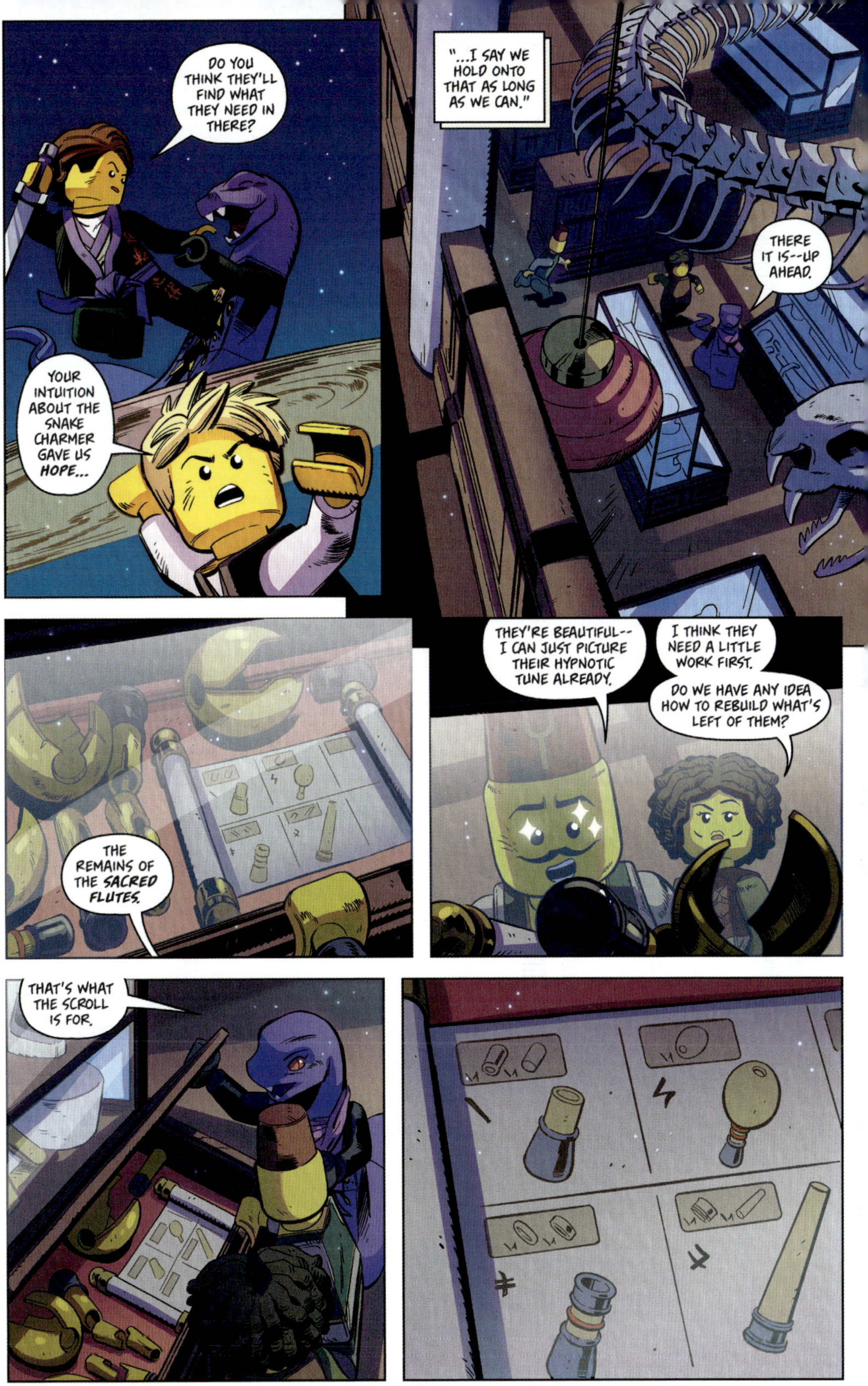
DO YOU THINK THEY'LL FIND WHAT THEY NEED IN THERE?
YOUR INTUITION ABOUT THE SNAKE CHARMER GAVE US HOPE...
"...I SAY WE HOLD ONTO THAT AS LONG AS WE CAN."
THERE IT IS--UP AHEAD.
THE REMAINS OF THE SACRED FLUTES.
THEY'RE BEAUTIFUL-- I CAN JUST PICTURE THEIR HYPNOTIC TUNE ALREADY.
I THINK THEY NEED A LITTLE WORK FIRST.
DO WE HAVE ANY IDEA HOW TO REBUILD WHAT'S LEFT OF THEM?
THAT'S WHAT THE SCROLL IS FOR.

WE NEED TO GET THESE TO THE OTHER MEMBERS OF THE ALLIANCE.
WE'LL USE THE MELODY TO PACIFY THE SERPENTINE LONG ENOUGH TO MAKE SURE WE CAN'T HARM ANYONE ELSE EVER AGAIN.
THE FLUTES WILL AFFECT EVERY SERPENTINE?
WHAT DOES THAT MEAN FOR YOU?
IT DOESN'T MATTER!

BECAUSE ALL OF YOU ARE DOOMED! ISN'T THAT RIGHT, CLOUSE?
INDEED, MASTER CHEN.
I AM SO DISAPPOINTED TO SEE YOU HERE, STRIKE. AFTER EVERYTHING WE DID FOR YOU! HOW COULD YOU?
ALL IT TOOK WAS REALIZING I'D BEEN PLAYED.
YES, YES. JUST LIKE ONE OF THOSE LITTLE FLUTES. BIG WHOOP!
THE SERPENTINE AND HUMANS HAD BEEN CIRCLING EACH OTHER FOR SO LONG, IT GOT BORING. ALL I DID WAS GIVE THEM A PUSH.
I NEEDED A SERPENTINE PRESENCE, AND YOUR TEDIOUS MONOLOGUES WERE PERFECT.
IT ALL WORKED BEAUTIFULLY! THE BATTLES, THE ADVENTURE, THE DRAMA! IT'S BEEN DELICIOUS.
THEN YOU STARTED TURNING YOUR NOSE UP AT THE WHOLE THING. I HOPED THE LIBRARY WOULD DISTRACT YOU.
BUT...YOUR IDEALS GOT IN THE WAY AGAIN. SO SAD.
YOU NEVER CARED ABOUT THE PROPHECY OF THE GOLDEN MASTER, OR THE ARTIFACTS OR ANY OF IT!
NO, NO. I CARE ABOUT MY FUTURE! I'M BUILDING A GRAND ENTERPRISE YOU COULDN'T FATHOM.
AND IT STARTS WITH THESE TOKENS OF THE PAST.

YOU COLLECT HISTORY, BUT THESE PLANTS HAVE SEEN ALL OF IT.
THE REAL TALE OF HISTORY IS ONE OF RENEWAL AND HOPE.
REBUILDING.
BUT WE'RE NOT ABOVE TEARING YOU DOWN FIRST!
SMASH

BAHAHA!
YOU'RE DELAYING THE INEVITABLE! MY ANACONDRAI WILL BE HERE ANY MOMENT NOW.
THE FLUTES!
!
NO SPEECHES THIS TIME...
JUST TEAMWORK.

BROTHER... I'M NOT SURE HOW MUCH LONGER WE CAN KEEP THIS UP.
IF THIS IS THE END...
...I AM GLAD YOU'RE BY MY SIDE. THE WAY IT **SHOULD** BE.
DO YOU...**HEAR** THAT?

IT'S THE FLUTES!
REMARKABLE. THE ANACONDRAI ARE COMPLETELY IMMOBILIZED.
THANKS TO THIS ONE'S SKILLS WITH A WOODWIND.
THE INSTRUMENTS ARE ASTOUNDING! THEY PRACTICALLY PLAY THEMSELVES.
ANYONE CAN DO IT.
WHAT DO YOU SAY WE PUT THAT THEORY TO THE TEST?

STRIKE?
STRIKE! YOU'RE ALRIGHT!
BUT HOW?
THERE WAS MORE TO THE STORY OF THE SACRED FLUTES THAN I REALIZED.

THE CONNECTION THEY BRING BETWEEN HUMANS AND SERPENTINE COMES ONLY IF IN YOUR HEART YOU ARE OPEN TO COMMUNICATION AND UNDERSTANDING.
IF ALL YOU SEEK IS TO CONTROL, THEN THAT WILL BE YOUR FATE.
FOR SO LONG, I DREAMED OF UNITING THE SERPENTINE. NOW, I'M CURSED TO BE SEPARATED FROM THEM FOREVER.

DAYS LATER IN THE COURT OF NINJAGO.
ORDER! WE WILL HAVE ORDER HERE!
KNOK KNOK
YOU, GENERALS OF THE ANACONDRAI FORCES, HAVE BEEN BROUGHT HERE TO FACE JUDGMENT FOR YOUR ACTIONS.
WE WERE MISLED--MANIPULATED BY THE SCHEMES OF A HUMAN! HE'S THE ONE YOU SHOULD BE PUNISHING!
I ASSURE YOU, GENERAL ARCTURUS...
"...HE WAS DEALT WITH."
SERIOUSLY? EXILE? THERE'S NO FUN IN THAT. NONE!
THAT'S THE IDEA.
HOPEFULLY IT'S A WARNING FOR ANY OTHER ALLIES OF MASTER CHEN STILL LURKING AMONG US.

AS FOR YOU GENERALS, YOUR QUEST FOR DOMINATION OVER NINJAGO HAS LEFT THE LAND AND ITS PEOPLE SPLINTERED.
REGARDLESS OF WHAT MADE YOU READY YOUR WEAPONS IN THE FIRST PLACE, HOW YOU USED THEM WAS ENTIRELY YOUR OWN DOING.
WE ASK...FOR MERCY.
MERCY?!
NEVER HEARD OF IT.
WE SENTENCE YOU TO BANISHMENT.
TO THE CURSED REALM.

SHOULD I NOT BE SENT TO THE CURSED REALM, AS WELL?
CHEN TOOK ADVANTAGE OF ME, BUT THE SAME CAN BE SAID OF THE ANACONDRAI GENERALS.
THE GENERALS WERE GIVEN AN OPPORTUNITY IN CHEN'S MEDDLING AND SOUGHT UTTER DOMINATION.
YOU DID NO SUCH THING, AS THE FLUTES CONFIRMED.
YOUR MISSION FROM THE START WAS UNITY.
BY WORKING WITH US, YOU PROVED AN ALLIANCE BETWEEN HUMANS AND SERPENTINE IS POSSIBLE.
I STILL HAVE HOPE THAT ONE DAY WE WILL SEE THE FRUITS OF THAT LABOR.
UNTIL THAT TIME, I KNOW NINJAGO IS BETTER OFF WITH YOU HERE.

I THINK THIS ALLIANCE HAS FORMED A BOND THAT WILL STAY WITH US.
GARMADON...DO YOU HAVE A MOMENT?
FOR YOU, MISAKO?
I HAVE ALL THE TIME IN THE WORLD.
SO...IT'S *OVER?*
THE FIGHTING *AND* THE ALLIANCE?
THE CONFLICT IS, *THANKFULLY,* AT AN END.
BUT, WHEN CALLED UPON, I *KNOW* OUR ALLIANCE WILL BE THERE FOR NINJAGO.

NOW.
DO YOU EVER SEE MEMBERS FROM THE OLD ALLIANCE?
SOMETIMES.
"MOST OFTEN I SEE THEM IN THE FACES OF THE NEXT GENERATION, WHO I'M NOW FORTUNATE ENOUGH TO TEACH."
THAT KEEPS MY SPIRITS UP. EVEN IF THEY MAKE ME FEEL OLDER EVERY DAY. HEH.
BUT WHATEVER'S COMING NOW HAS YOUR SPIRITS... ***WANING?***
IT MUST BE QUITE THE THREAT IF YOU FIND YOURSELF REVISITING ***OUR*** OLD BATTLES.

IT'S MY RESPONSIBILITY TO PASS ON WHAT I KNOW. BUT AFTER SO MUCH CONFLICT...
I FIND IT HARD TO ASSURE THEM THAT THINGS WILL BE ALRIGHT AFTER THIS LATEST STORM.
THERE WILL ALWAYS BE UNCERTAINTY. I'VE MADE PEACE WITH THAT. THERE ARE ONLY TWO THINGS THAT MATTER.
FIRST-- WHO IS BY YOUR SIDE? ARE THEY PEOPLE YOU TRUST? PEOPLE WHO CARE FOR THE WELLBEING OF OTHERS?
WITHOUT QUESTION.

ALL THAT'S LEFT THEN, IS WHAT YOU'RE FIGHTING FOR.
PEACE.
IT'S ALWAYS WORTH STRIVING FOR, NO MATTER HOW LONG IT LASTS. WHEN WE KNOW THAT TO BE TRUE...
...PERHAPS THEN, MY FRIEND, WE TOO CAN BE AT PEACE.
The End.

GARMADON
WILL RETURN

SKETCHBOOK

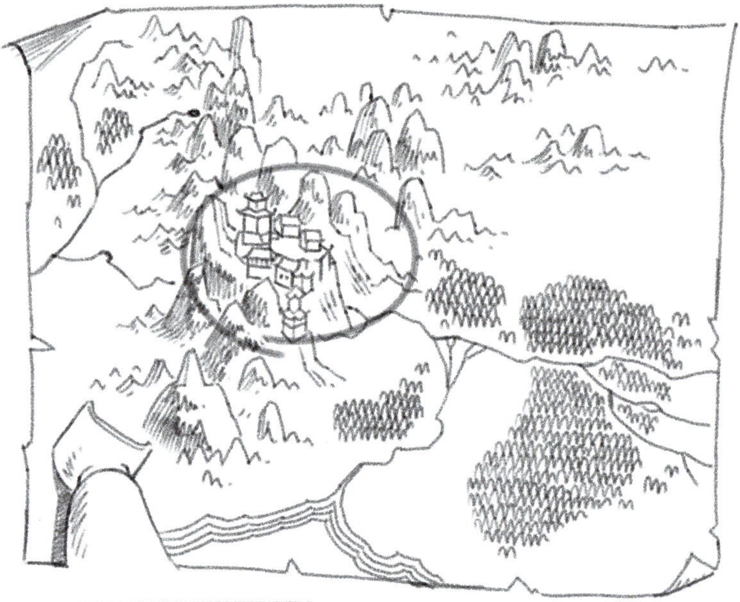

LEGO NINJAGO	ENVIRONMENT DESIGN
THE SERPENTINE WAR	MAP OF JAMANAKAI VILLAGE

Will created many detailed and stunning concept pieces while creating the art for STRIKE OF THE SERPENTINE. Here's a look at some of them!

ANACONDRAI PATTERN

STRIKE ALTERNATIVE PATTERN

Character designs for Brook, the Master of Nature

Character design for Leo, the Master of Form

LEGO NINJAGO	ENVIRONMENT DESIGN
THE SERPENTINE WAR	EMERALD FOREST GREENHOUSE

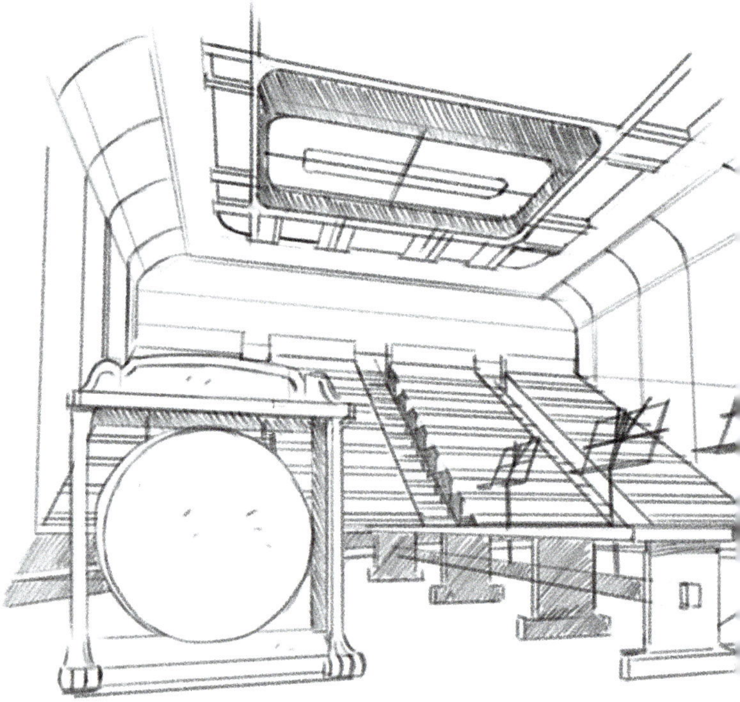

LEGO NINJAGO	ENVIRONMENT DESIGN
THE SERPENTINE WAR	THE LOST MELODY MUSIC HALL

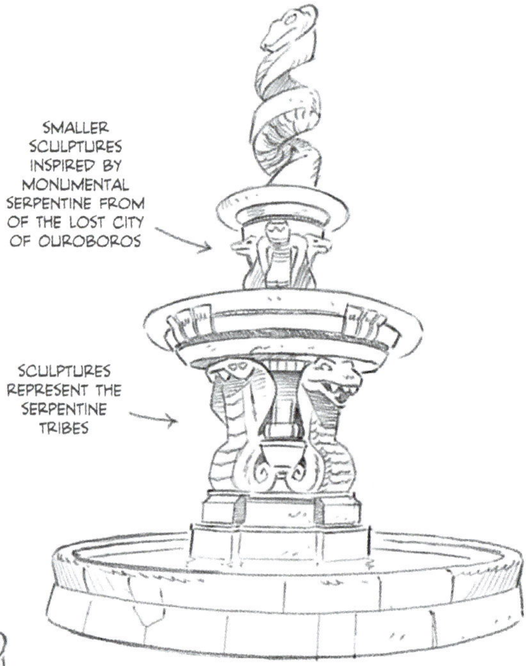

Details on the designs for the Serpentine fountain

Chapter 1 Title Page Inks

Chapter 2 Title Page Inks

Chapter 3 Title Page Inks

Chapter 4 Title Page Inks

Chapter 5 Title Page Inks

LEGO® NINJAGO®: STRIKE OF THE SERPENTINE

CAMERON CHITTOCK WRITER
WILL MORRIS ARTIST, COVER
SARA ANTONELLINI COLORIST
PAT BROSSEAU LETTERER
NACHIE MARSHAM & AMANDA LAFRANCO EDITORS
ANDRES JUAREZ STRIKE OF THE SERPENTINE LOGO
JILLIAN CRAB COLLECTION DESIGN & PRODUCTION

SPECIAL THANKS TO AMEET'S PAWEL GRZEGORCZYK, MAGDALENA CZYZEWSKA, ALISON LINDSAY, CINDY LOH, ALEKSANDRA RAJEWSKA, JAKUB NIEDZIELSKI, PIOTR PACZKOWSKI, ULRICH SCHROEDER, PAWEL MUDZA, AND DAN SHEPHERD, AND LEGO GROUP'S LYDIA BARRAM, ASHLEY BLAIS, HELLE REIMERS HOLM-JØRGENSEN, TOMMY KALMAR AND MARTIN LEIGHTON LINDHARDT FOR THEIR INVALUABLE ASSISTANCE.

MIX
Paper | Supporting responsible forestry
FSC® C144528
www.fsc.org

BOOKS

Manufactured by AMEET Sp. z o.o. under license from the LEGO Group.

AMEET Sp. z o.o.
Nowe Sady 6, 94-102 Łódź – Poland
ameet@ameet.eu
www.ameet.eu

www.LEGO.com

LEGO® NINJAGO®: STRIKE OF THE SERPENTINE. First Printing.
ISBN: 978-1-5343-3335-2
Published in United States and Canada by Image Comics, Inc. Office of Publication: PO BOX 14457, Portland, OR 97293.